THE RAILWAY EMPIRE

THE RAILWAY EMPIRE

Anthony Burton

JOHN MURRAY

The author and publishers would like to thank the following for giving their permission to reproduce photographs: Plate 1: Timothy Hackworth Victorian and Railway Museum; Plate 2: W.W. Stewart Collection; Plate 3: author's collection; Plate 4: Tyne and Wear Archives; Plates 5, 6, 7, 8, 9, 11, 21, 22, 23, 24: Institution of Civil Engineers; Plates 10, 12, 13, 17, 18, 19: Royal Commonwealth Society Library; Plates 14, 15, 16, 20: Crown Agents.

First published in 1994
by John Murray (Publishers) Ltd.,
50 Albemarle Street, London W1X 4BD

A catalogue record for this book is available from the British Library

ISBN 0-7195-5170-6

Typeset in 11½/13½ pt Times Roman
by Colset Pte Ltd, Singapore
Printed and bound in Great Britain by Cambridge University Press, Cambridge

Contents

Illustrations

(between pages 120 and 121)

vi

Preface

As work was coming to an end on *The Railway Builders*, John Murray suggested that I might like to widen the scope to look at the work of Britons in building railways around the world in the nineteenth century. I was – and am – grateful to him for the idea. However, had I known when I started just how much work was entailed my gratitude would have been touched with dismay. It is a vast subject, and this book does not pretend to cover every single line in which there was a British interest. To do so would, I believe, make it too specialist and to the general reader, tedious. What I have tried to do is to give enough information so that the reader can appreciate the range of problems faced by different railway builders in different times and the ways in which they tackled them. The final results were often stupendous although the cost in labour immense. As that doyen of authors on engineering history L.T.C. Rolt wrote in the last volume of his autobiography, *Landscape With Figures*: 'the whole art of research is knowing when to stop.' I tried to stop at that critical point when, although new material was still turning up, it was merely facts and stories already noted in what had become a daunting pile of material. My notes are legion compared with the finished book. Finally, for reasons of simplicity and consistency I decided to refer to countries by the names under which they were known at the time the railways were built – Moldavia not Romania, for example, and Rhodesia not Zimbabwe.

I could never have completed this work without a great deal

of help. First on the list is my wife and working partner, Pip Burton, who took on much of the labour of tracking down sources and helped in many other ways. I also owe a special debt of gratitude to Mary Murphy and Mike Chrimes of The Institution of Civil Engineers and Theo Dunnet of the Radcliffe Science Library.

Anthony Burton
Bristol, 1993

CHAPTER ONE

Beginnings

This is a story of great adventures, of men in sola topees hacking their way through the jungles of uncharted lands. It is a tale of epic proportions, of armies of men travelling half-way round the world to shovel foreign soil into English wheelbarrows. It is also a story of high finance, of millions being raised in London for such exotic sounding enterprises as the Ferrocarril al Oeste or the Bombay, Baroda and Central Indian Railway. The crest of the latter hangs by my desk showing four Indian porters staggering up a stony path under the weight of an ornate palanquin, while a resplendent train puffs its way over a viaduct behind them, the driver leaning nonchalantly out of his cab window. Somehow it seems to sum up much of what one thinks of as the great railway empire: the old giving way to the new, the splendours of British manufacture looking down, literally and metaphorically, on the crudities of an older world. But how did all this come about? It is not difficult to imagine why British India should turn to the British engineer for help, but why should the French, the Russians, the Argentinians and the Japanese have turned in the same direction for manpower, machines and money to build their railways? It is too easy to say 'because Britain was first', too easy and not altogether true.

The story begins in Germany. Georg Bauer was a mining engineer who spent his life recording the best mining techniques of the age. In 1556, a year after his death, his work appeared in print, in suitably classical guise, as Agricola's *De Re Metallica*.

It features superb woodcuts illustrating the machinery of the mines, among which scurry the miners themselves. If they seem mildly comical today, that is because they have comical associations. Walt Disney used these drawings as the basis for the costumes of the Seven Dwarfs: the first known illustration of a railway shows a truck being handled by a close relation of Happy, Sleepy and Dopey. The system Bauer showed is not strictly speaking a railway, as the wheels run on planks and the trucks are kept in place by a pin running in a groove on the track, but the elements of a railway were certainly there, half a century before there is a record of anything of the sort appearing in Britain. When that happened, however, the system was so evidently superior to the earlier model that it became generally accepted in the mining community, and even the Germans knew it as the 'Englischer Kohlenweg'.

The earliest records of this type of railway system date from the early 1600s. Huntingdon Beaumont was both colliery owner and engineer. Some time in 1603 he laid down approximately two miles of track from the pithead of his colliery at Wollaton near Nottingham. The track was still wooden, but now there was no plank and groove; this track consisted of rails on which trucks ran with double-flanged wheels, looking very similar to ordinary pulley-wheels. There were other routes in Shropshire, but the most popular area for the new 'wagon-ways', as they soon became known, were the coalfields of the north-east of England. By the middle of the eighteenth century, the system was already sufficiently interesting to foreign engineers for them to wish to inspect it. Among these was a Frenchman, Monsieur Jars, who came over in 1765 and wrote a description of what he saw, entitled *Voyages Metallurgiques*. The '*nouvelles routes*' ran from pits near to the river bank, where the trucks could be unloaded into waiting ships that took the coal round the coast. The trucks were arranged on a gradual, steady descent so that gravity did most of the work, and they could be hauled back by horses. The system had squared-off rails, 6 or 7 inches broad by 4 or 5 inches thick, carried on parallel rows of oak sleepers, 4 to 8 inches square. The rails were held together by wooden pins, and the joints were

2

protected by iron strips. By the time of Jars' visit, there was already a movement towards replacing the old wooden wagon wheels by cast-iron. The wagons were fitted with a hinged bottom, which would be knocked open at the riverside staithes, allowing the whole load to be deposited into a chute. It was also not unknown for the flap to be jolted open in transit, dumping the coal on to the track resulting in what locals called a 'cold cake'.

By the end of the eighteenth century the simple wagon-ways were becoming increasingly sophisticated. The improvement in iron making that began with the Darbys of Coalbrookdale made it possible to improve the track by laying a metal strip over the wood and eventually to replace the wood altogether by metal. Again many of the early experiments came in the colliery districts. In 1776 the mining engineer John Curr introduced the metal plateway to the underground workings. The rails, or plates, had an L-shaped cross-section, which held the wagon to the track. Previously, coal had been moved from the face in baskets, man-handled, or rather child-handled since most of the work went to boys and girls, along the low, narrow galleries. The plateway represented such an immense improvement, and saved so much grindingly hard labour that Curr found himself celebrated in verse – with a suitably Geordie accent.

> God bless the man wi' peace and plenty
> That first invented metal plates,
> Draw out his years to five times twenty,
> Then slide him through the heavenly gates.
>
> For if the human frame to spare
> Frae toil an' pain ayont conceevin'
> Hae aught te de wi' gettin' there,
> Aw think he mun gan' strite to heaven.

The simple plateway soon became part of a complex web of railways, requiring ever more elaborate engineering works. As early as the 1720s one of these lines, the Tanfield tramway in

County Durham, had to be taken across the Houghwell Burn, where it carves its way through a deep, wooded valley. The job of bridging the gap went to a local mason, Ralph Wood, who designed a bridge as a single, graceful span of 103 feet. And there it stands today, the world's oldest surviving railway bridge. Although the plateway or tramway system was developing rapidly, the greatest changes in the field of transport came with the spread of canals from 1760 onwards. A horse pulling a boat or a barge could shift far more cargo than a horse hauling wagons on even the best made tramway. Locks conquered the problem of hills; valleys were crossed on high embankments and soaring aqueducts; hills pierced by cuttings and tunnels. The engineering skills that were to be vital in the railway age of the nineteenth century were being learned in the canal age of the eighteenth. But there were places where even the most ambitious canal engineer could never take a waterway. The valleys of South Wales, for example, run largely parallel to each other in a north-south direction, separated by high spines of hills. East-west connections brought engineers such as Benjamin Outram to construct tramways to link industry to canal and one canal to another.

The surprise is, in some ways, that so many of these advances were occurring in Britain. An unbiased observer casting his eye over Europe at the beginning of the eighteenth century would probably have elected the French for the role of great engineering innovators. The British marvelled at the privately financed Bridgewater Canal in 1760 with its aqueduct over the River Irwell, yet a century earlier, in the 1660s, the French had already built the Languedoc Canal, 150 miles long with 100 locks, a tunnel and three major aqueducts. British engineers had, in effect, been reinventing the wheel. The work on the canal was organized with great professionalism by Pierre-Paul Riquet, and at one time 8000 men were employed in the works. Voltaire went to view the Louvre and Versailles, but he said, *'le monument le plus glorieux par son utilité, par sa grandeur, et par ses difficultés, fut ce canal de Languedoc qui joint les deux mers'*.

The French worked in a systematic and orderly way and were soon to become the first European country to put the profession of engineering on to an official footing. The Corps des Ponts et Chaussées was formed in 1716 to supervise public works. Just as importantly, the French, unlike the pragmatic British, established an engineering school to train the next generation of builders. So important were the Ecole and the Corps that British engineers who wanted to remain up to date in their field and, just as importantly, wanted to grasp the theoretic basis of their subject, had no option but to learn French. France it seemed was leading the world in engineering and science. Yet by the 1830s when two Hungarian noblemen wanted to find the best way of building a bridge across the Danube in order to unite the cities of Buda and Pest, they had no doubt that the thing to do was to go to England, 'there consulting with men of experience and skill', because 'far more has been done there worth going to see, than is to be met with on the whole continent of Europe'. What had happened in the century between? The short answer is the French Revolution. While the French were preoccupied with overturning the social order which had given birth to the strict formalism of the Ponts et Chaussées, the British had been transforming the old economic order of their country in the Industrial Revolution.

The British invented little that was new in terms of the civil engineering of railways; they did, however, rapidly come to lead the world in the development of the invention that was to combine with the railway to create a whole new transport system: the steam engine. Once again the early experimental work occurred in continental Europe, while the British led the way in finding practical applications of steam power. It all began with the discovery that the atmosphere exerted pressure, first demonstrated by Evangelista Torricelli, a pupil of Galileo in 1643, and it was soon realized that if a vacuum could be created on one side of a piston, air pressure would work on the other side to drive it into the piston. The Dutchman Christiaan Huygens produced his vacuum by the alarming device of exploding gunpowder, but it was his assistant Denis Papin who first suggested the more sensible solution of condensing steam. His little demonstration engine was a curiosity – the only practical device he came up with was the pressure cooker. It was left principally to Thomas Newcomen

5

to use the same idea to produce a practical engine for pumping water from mines. His steam engine was soon nodding its ponderous head over mines all over Britain. This was the beam engine, where pump rods at one end of a beam dropped under their own weight, to be hauled up again by the piston attached to the other. It was a cumbersome process with steam in the cylinder being sprayed with cold water to condense it, after which air pressure worked on the open top cylinder. It was hugely expensive in terms of fuel, which was no great problem in the middle of a coal field, but which made it ruinously expensive in the coal starved areas of the metal mining regions.

A solution was found by James Watt, who realized that the steam could be condensed in a separate condenser outside the cylinder. This meant it was no longer necessary to alternately heat and cool the main cylinder. It also meant that he could use the steam on either side of the piston. The atmospheric pressure engine had become a steam engine proper, but was still using the notion of condensing the steam rather than using the pressure of the steam itself. But James Watt firmly believed that high-pressure steam was a dangerous monster – he would have none of it. And since he had acquired a patent that virtually excluded everyone else from making any kind of steam engine whatsoever, he ensured that the monster was kept caged until the patent expired in 1800. The Watt engine, however, was already a versatile machine, and the closed cylinder meant that the piston could be made to work in two directions, not just in one as in the Newcomen engine. It was not much of an imaginative leap to see that if you attached a crank you could turn a wheel: you could use it to work machinery in a factory, to turn the paddle wheels of a boat on water or even to turn the wheels of a vehicle on land.

The first vehicle to be moved over land by steam power was demonstrated in Paris in 1769 by its inventor Nicholas Cugnot. It was an extraordinary looking object with three wheels and a huge boiler that hung over the solitary front wheel. It was a masterpiece of instability as it proved after a few tottering metres of movement when it tumbled over amidst much hissing of steam

6

and showering of sparks. Monsieur Cugnot was not encouraged to continue with his experiment. James Watt himself contemplated a steam carriage, but his nervousness about the dangers of high-pressure steam prevented him from holding any trials. His bolder employee, William Murdock, was less reluctant and his model bowled cheerily down an English lane in 1784. The only acknowledgement he received was a prompt warning that any more tampering with such devices would see him out of a job. Matters had reached an impasse, but if the road engine was temporarily stymied, steam was beginning to find its place on the infant railway system of Britain.

The tramways serving the canals often included quite steep inclines on which the descent was controlled by a brake-man, in theory at least. The Duke of Rutland visited South Wales in the first decade of the nineteenth century and described the system he found at work on the tramway linking the Brecon and Abergavenny Canal to a local iron works.

This rail-road is adapted to the size of the waggons, or carts, which convey the coal to the canal. On each side is an iron groove, which extends the whole length of the road, and on which the wheels (four or six in number) run. They are so contrived as to run downwards the whole way (sometimes for the extent of some miles) from the works; so that when laden, they require no horses to draw them down. Indeed they acquire so great a degree of velocity in their descent, that a man is forced to walk or run behind the cart, with a kind of rudder or pole affixed to the hind-wheel, which he locks up when it proceeds too fast. Should this pole break (which it sometimes does) the waggon flies away, and overturns everything it meets. Of course, any one who is coming up the road, is in imminent danger, unless he can by any means get out of the way; which is very difficult, as the road is narrow, and runs along a precipice. Last year, Mr. Frere, the proprietor of the iron works, was returning from London, and going along the rail-road in a post-chaise, when about a hundred yards from him, he saw one of those

7

waggons coming down upon him with astonishing velocity. He could not possibly get out of the way, and must have been crushed to pieces, if fortunately the waggon had not broken over the iron groove, which had hitherto kept it in the track, and run forcibly up an ash-tree by the side of the road, in the branches of which it literally stuck, and thus saved him from immediate destruction.

One way of avoiding this alarming situation was to control the movement by cable and drum, with the added advantage that if two tracks were built, the weight of the full trucks going down could be used to lift the empties back up again. This was fine as long as the tramways were always working downhill, but it was clear that the problem could be overcome by combining winding drum and stationary steam engine. So it was that in many mines, men became used to working with the new machines, whether pumping water from the pit, raising and lowering men and materials, or acting as a motive power for the trucks of a tramway system. These were not 'educated men' in the conventional sense – such education as they had came from practical experience. They were often openly scornful of the advantages of any other form of education, no matter how grand they themselves were: the great civil engineer John Rennie declared that 'after a young man has been three or four years at the University of Oxford or Cambridge, he cannot, without much difficulty turn himself to the practical part of civil engineering'. Rennie might have taken a more charitable view of the French engineering school, but there was still nothing of the sort to be found in Britain. The future of the steam railway was to lie in the hands of men such as George Stephenson, who received no formal schooling at all and started his working life at the age of eight. Stephenson, however, was by no means the first in the field of steam locomotion. That story really begins in 1800.

In 1800 the Boulton and Watt patent at last expired and the way to experimentation lay officially open. Nowhere was the news greeted with more enthusiasm than among the tin and copper mines of Cornwall. With no local source of fuel, they were desperate to find more efficient ways of using steam than those offered by Watt and his condenser. One answer was 'strong steam', or high-pressure steam, and there was no more enthusiastic advocate than the young son of a mine 'captain', Richard Trevithick. He was twenty-six years old when he began his experiments in 1797, and he was soon trying out his first road locomotive. On Christmas Eve 1801 his little engine successfully pulled a party of local worthies up a hill near Camborne. It was a great success – up to a point. The engine hit a gulley and the steering mechanism was damaged. His companion Davies Gilbert related what happened next: 'The carriage was forced under some shelter, and the Partners adjourned to the Hotel, & comforted their hearts with a Roast Goose and proper drinks, when, forgetfull of the Engine, its Water boiled away, the Iron became red hot, and nothing that was combustible remained either of the Engine or the house.'

Trevithick continued despite this somewhat inauspicious beginning, and built another road engine which trundled around the streets of London, without it appears exciting any enthusiasm in anyone. It is interesting, if no more, to think what the future of transport might have been had the road engine been a success. Trevithick was not a man temperamentally inclined, however, to dwell on failures or to pursue his notions beyond what he considered a reasonable distance. He paid a visit to Coalbrookdale, with its extensive tramway, and there it seems possible that he made tentative experiments in putting his steam locomotive on rails. But the great event finally occurred in 1804.

Trevithick had sold a share of his patent in the road locomotive to a Welsh ironmaster, Samuel Homfray. Partly to publicize the engine, and partly because it seemed a good bet anyway, Homfray made a wager of 500 guineas that the locomotive could haul a load of 10 tons along the Penydarren tramway that ran from a point near Merthyr Tydfil for nearly 10 miles to Abercynon and the Glamorgan Canal. It is still possible to walk much of the route of the old line, where lines of stone sleeper blocks lie embedded in the ground, and imagine the scene when the tiny locomotive came panting its way up the lonely valley of the River Taff. Gilbert again was on hand to record the event.

> Yesterday we proceeded on our journey with the engine; we carry'd ten tons of Iron, five waggons, and 70 men riding on them the whole of the journey. Its about nine miles which we perform'd in 4 hours & 5 Mints [*sic*], but we had to cut down some trees and remove some large rocks out of the road.

The engine was a success: the railway was not. The cast-iron rails cracked under the weight of the engine, which rather spoiled the experiment. In many ways the Penydarren engine showed its pioneering nature in devices such as the huge cumbersome flywheel; in other ways it was to foreshadow later developments. The exhaust steam was turned up the chimney to increase the blast to the fire, a device that was to be reinvented by George Stephenson a decade later. Trevithick was able to sell one of his locomotives to the collieries of the north-east, but the Wylam tramway proved as inappropriate as the Penydarren for taking the weight and force of a locomotive. The engine suffered the indignity of being taken off its wheels and used as a primitive stationary engine. Trevithick was to make one last bid to get publicity for his invention, by running an engine round a circular track near the site of the present Euston station. 'Catch-me-who-can', as it was called, was unfortunately looked on more as an amusing side-show exhibit than a serious form of transport. The world did not rush to Trevithick's door demanding steam locomotives, and he turned his inventive genius to other applications of high-pressure steam. It was not quite the end of Richard Trevithick's involvement with railways and steam locomotives. The world did at least recognize him as a master of steam and he was recruited to build engines for the silver mines of Peru in 1816. He had years of great success, but then war ravished the industry and he reached Cartagena on his way home in 1827, an impoverished, but far from broken man. There he met a young Englishman, whom he had dandled on his knee when he had taken his colliery engine to Tyneside, Robert Stephenson.

Trevithick was returning to an uncertain future; Stephenson was going home to work on the great Liverpool & Manchester Railway. There can scarcely have been a more poignantly symbolic moment than this: the young man who was shortly to design the *Rocket* had to lend the inventor of the steam locomotive £50 to get home. It might have been a consolation to know that future Trevithicks were to be among the band of engineers who were to go on to build railways for the world.

Steam locomotive development was undoubtedly held back by the brittle cast-iron track. In 1808 John Blenkinsop took over a colliery near Leeds and one of the problems he faced was the high cost of getting coal from pit head to the River Aire. The cost of fodder during the Napoleonic Wars made horse transport on the Middleton Colliery railway very expensive and Blenkinsop favoured steam – but what to do about the broken rails? He took the problem to a local engineer, Matthew Murray, whose enthusiasm for steam was well known – his house was even called Steam Hall. He realized that only by building a lighter engine could the permanent way be saved from breaking up every time a train passed over it. But light engines could not pull heavy loads. The answer was to find a way of increasing the tractive power. He designed a rack-and-pinion engine, of the sort still used on mountain railways throughout the world. It was suggested by some later commentators that Murray believed smooth wheels would slip on smooth rails but this was never the case. What Murray came up with was a practical solution to a very real problem. The 5-ton engine could haul around 15 tons without the rack-and-pinion – with it the load went up to 90 tons, and no smashed rails.

The Middleton Colliery Railway was a triumph. Thousands came to see it run, but more importantly a regular service was in operation by 1812 with two locomotives. Two more were added the following year. This was no gimmick, but a genuine commercial steam railway. It attracted immense interest and not just from local sightseers. George Stephenson came down from Tyneside to take a look in 1813, and the next year he built his very own first locomotive for Killingworth colliery. It cannot be pure coincidence that the main dimensions – piston diameter, stroke, boiler size, flue diameter – were virtually the same in the Murray and the Stephenson engine. And now, for the very first time, the wider world began to pay attention. Grand Duke Nicholas of Russia, soon to become Emperor, made the pilgrimage to the Yorkshire colliery in 1816 and according to local reports showed a 'curious appreciation and an expression of no small admiration'. But already the Middleton Railway had become obsolete, overtaken by an improvement in rail technology which had made heavier locomotives viable and the rack-and-pinion redundant.

Early locomotive development now became centred on the collieries of the north-east. There were a good many developments between the years 1813 and 1815, with numerous engineers putting forward ideas, but for the next decade there was only one man in England, or indeed the world, actively engaged in designing and building locomotives, George Stephenson. He received some encouragement. One fanatical railway prophet was Thomas Gray of Nottingham, regarded by some of his contemporaries as certifiably lunatic. He actually suggested covering the whole country with a network of railways carrying freight and, even more astonishingly, passengers. His book of 1820, *Observations on a General Iron-Railway*, has a frontispiece showing a Murray-type locomotive chuffing along with what can only be called three stage coaches, complete with horn-tooting postilions. His vision was neatly expressed in a short verse on the title page.

No speed with this, can swiftest horse compare;
No weight like this, canal or vessel bear
As this will commerce every way promote
To this, let sons of commerce grant their vote.

Contemporaries were unimpressed. John Francis writing of Gray in 1851, said: 'With one consent he was voted an intolerable bore'. But the intolerable bore was to see the first step being taken towards the realization of his dream in 1825.

The Stockton & Darlington Railway has gone down in history as the first public railway to be built specifically with steam

12

locomotives in mind and to be designed to carry both passengers and freight, which is certainly true enough. But such a simple statement tends to mask the fact that it was essentially still a half-way house on the road to a wholly modern railway system: it was a colliery line writ large. For a start, hills were still overcome by inclines along which trains were hauled by cable, and although freight was shifted by steam, the first passengers were carried in what was in effect a stage coach with flanged wheels, pulled by a horse. It fell short even of Gray's fantasy railway. Stephenson designed new locomotives, but they featured very little in the way of improvements over what had gone before. But in the end it was not so much what the Stockton & Darlington was that counted, as what it was seen to be. It was perceived as something wholly new. Henry Booth who was to become treasurer to the Liverpool & Manchester Railway, and an engineering innovator in his own right, described it as 'the great theatre of practical operations upon railways'. It was an international theatre as well: visitors came from all over Europe, and they included the French engineer Marc Seguin, who was to share with Booth and Robert Stephenson the honour of producing the first multi-tubed boilers. The grandly named Pennsylvania Society for the Promotion of Internal Improvement sent over William Strickland to see what all the fuss was about. A climate was being created in which railways could grow. Within the next ten years railways were to open in France, Belgium, Germany and North America, and work would have begun in many more. And the call went out for the British to help build them.

It is not difficult to see why British steam locomotives were in demand: the British were the only people in the world building them. One of the first things the astute George Stephenson did following the success of the Stockton & Darlington Railway was to establish a locomotive works in the name of his son, Robert – and Robert was not to disappoint him. Although 1825 had been a triumph, not everyone was convinced that steam locomotives would provide the power – and certainly not all the power – for a railway system. When the Liverpool & Manchester was begun, hard on the heels of the Stockton & Darlington, there was still a faction that wanted to see trains hauled by cable, passing on from stationary engine to stationary engine. There was a strong feeling that interesting though the steam locomotive was as a novelty, it was not really up to the task. That question was decisively answered in the famous Rainhill Trials of 1829. The nature of the test was clearly spelled out. A 6-ton locomotive had to show itself 'capable of drawing after it, day by day, on a well-constructed Railway, on a level plane, a Train of Carriages of the gross weight of Twenty Tons, including the Tender and Water Tank, at a rate of Ten Miles per Hour, with a pressure of steam in the boiler not exceeding Fifty Pounds on the square inch'. There were to be three serious contenders. Timothy Hackworth, locomotive superintendent of the Stockton & Darlington Railway, built *Sans Pareil* at the company's Shildon works – at his own expense. It was a sturdy engine using what were then well established principles, but failed at the trials when a cylinder cracked. John Braithwaite and John Ericsson's privately constructed *Novelty* looked the greyhound of the pack, but was to prove fatally short of stamina; and there was *Rocket*, built at the Stephensons' own Newcastle factory. *Rocket* contained all the principal design features that were to form the basis for locomotive design for the remainder of the century. The engine not only managed 10 miles an hour, it positively flew along at 30 m.p.h.; and the plans for cable-worked inclines were quickly scrapped when *Rocket* tore up the slopes, with huge *élan*. No wonder engineers all over the world were unanimous that for a time, at least, British really was best.

The actual technology of locomotive construction was not immensely complicated; hence there seems no good reason why overseas engineers should not speedily follow where Stephenson, Hackworth and others had led. Had there been a mechanical engineering school in France similar to their school of bridges and roads, no doubt they would have quickly followed. But this was not the case.

The locomotive evolved slowly from the giant pumping engines that drained mines and its development ran parallel with the life of its principal developer, George Stephenson. Born in 1781, a collier's son, he followed his father to the pit, being placed in charge of a winding engine that lifted men and coal from pit bottom to the surface, a responsible job which he was given at the age of just seventeen. He soon showed himself to be a resourceful practical engineer, able to spot problems when engines went wrong and devise methods of overcoming them, yet this expertise came from native wit and experience. He had virtually no formal education and was, at best, semi-literate.

In 1812, a violent explosion at the Felling colliery resulted in the deaths of ninety-two men and boys. It was due to the lethal combination of 'fire damp' – methane gas – and naked lamps. A committee was set up offering a prize for a safety lamp. One of the winners was Sir Humphry Davy, who applied scientific principles in designing a lamp which was named after him. The other was George Stephenson, who employed trial and error, even to the point of taking his own lamp down to a spot where 'a blower' was sending out great gusts of gas. Had he been wrong, Stephenson would never have built a railway, or anything else, ever again. The interesting feature here is Davy's reaction. He absolutely refused to believe that an illiterate collier was capable of such a thing, and when the mine managers of the north-east raised a special fund for Stephenson, he was incensed. He railed against the address of thanks 'which every Man of Science in the Kingdom knows to be as fake in substance as it is absurd in expression.' Practical working men could not possibly be the equal of educated men of science. But it was practical working men who were to develop the steam locomotive.

As Stephenson continued to rise in the colliery world, other men of similar background were also doing innovative work. Trevithick had sent his locomotive up to Christopher Blackett of the Wylam colliery, and Blackett in his turn encouraged his manager William Hedley to try his hand at engine design. The result was hard-working, sturdy engines like *Puffing Billy*, which with numerous modifications was to go on puffing right up to 1860. And Hedley brought in others to help. The Wylam blacksmith Timothy Hackworth joined in the exciting new work and though he was to be disappointed at Rainhill, he was to go on to build magnificent engines of great power, starting with the innovative *Royal George*. All these men shared the same background – strong on practice, virtually bereft of theory. George Stephenson had enough sense to see that his son Robert obtained a great deal more formal education than he had ever had, right up to university. Robert went to Edinburgh, the place with the highest reputation for science, but was unimpressed by what he learned there. University science came a poor second to the practical science of engineering works and mines. In 1822, he wrote a letter to an old family friend.

Mr Jameson's Lectures have hitherto been confined chiefly to Zoology, a part of Natural History which I cannot say I am enraptured with; nor can I infer from many of his Lectures any ultimate benefit, unless to satisfy the curiosity of man. Natural historians spend a great deal of time in enquiring whether Adam was a black or white man. Now I really cannot see what better we should be, if we could even determine this with satisfaction; but our limited knowledge will always place this question in the shade of darkness. The Professor puzzles me sadly with his Latin appellations of the various divisions, species, genera, &c., of the animal kingdom. He lectures two days a week on Meteorology and three on Zoology. This makes the course very unconnected.

I have taken notes on Natural Philosophy, but have not written them out, as there has been nothing but the simplest parts, and which I was perfectly acquainted with.

There was no denying it, advances in the early days of the railways were the result of the practical experiences of working men – and that experience was most readily available in Britain. America, already showing its new spirit of independence, was to be one of the few countries that was to employ home-built locomotives from the start, but then an American, Oliver Evans, had taken his steam vehicle out on the road as early as 1804. It was not, of course, simply knowhow that was required, there had to be the industrial base there as well. That meant power and iron and engineering works, all of which Britain had been building up during the dramatic, and often traumatic, years of the Industrial Revolution. Britain had not just produced the first successful steam locomotive, it was also home to the first iron bridges, the first iron boat and a whole range of inventions and innovations. Yet this is only part of the story of the Railway Empire. Britain could, and indeed did, take a role as the engineering workshop for that Empire, shipping out locomotives to the rest of the world. But the world wanted more. Countries on every continent turned to Britain to build their railways, survey the routes, design their viaducts, dig out the ground and hack through the rock. Surprisingly,often they wanted Britain to find the money to pay for their railways as well. This, on the face of it, may seem strange. To find out why one has again to turn back to a period before the railway age began.

The French had, as we have seen, a great tradition of canal building. The British were slow to follow their lead. Once they did, however, they did so with immense energy, developing a huge and complex network of canals. What is of interest here is how these canals (and then railways) were financed.

A canal was not like a factory or mill. You could not just set up a canal in a modest way and use the profits to develop the business. Canals required very large capital sums indeed, running into hundreds of thousands of pounds, millions in today's terms. Allowing promoters to encourage the public to invest in such projects with promises of large profits was an obvious solution, but the South Sea Bubble had shown that the public was, alas, just as willing to invest in a hopeless scheme as a sound one. Following this disaster, the government stepped in to regulate investment. Although canals were largely built by joint-stock companies, before anything could be done a scheme had to be approved by Act of Parliament. The company and its plans were subject to parliamentary scrutiny. It was not a fool-proof system, but it did offer the investors some guarantee that a disinterested third party had given the plans consideration and approved them as practical. In fact, companies regularly underestimated the construction costs by an alarming amount and overestimated

17

the profits similarly. The relevant point is that a method had been found for financing very large capital projects, and on the whole it worked. The canals were built, and the best of them provided handsome dividends. A public had appeared that was quite ready to invest in such major capital projects. In the early days of French canal construction, the costs were born by the state; in Britain they were carried by a variety of people, ranging from speculators to sober industrialists. As the lure of the canals began to fade, these investors happily switched to railways. And the railways did not have to be on British soil.

The engineers of the canal age had shown themselves more than competent, and men such as Jessop, Telford and Rennie rose to international as well as local fame. Civil engineering was put on a professional basis with the founding of the Institution of Civil Engineers in 1820. Thomas Telford was its first president. It became not so much a forum for ideas as a collecting house for practical projects. Telford wrote to Count von Platen of Sweden, who had invited him to work on the Gotha Canal in 1808, to ask for material to be sent to the library, but made it very clear precisely what was wanted: 'You will remind them to send me drawings and descriptions of works really executed. We have no wish for learned discussions; facts and practical operations are to compose our collections and we should leave project and theory to those who are disposed to create new systems.' There speaks the voice of the pragmatic British engineer, the man who had worked his way up from humble beginnings to the highest pinnacle of his profession, the very model of Samuel Smiles' self-made man. To a large extent it was this quality that made the British engineer so popular with overseas promoters. He might not have been able to supply written answers to examination papers – some of the older generation of engineers could scarcely have read the questions – but he got ten out of ten in the practicals. He could be relied on to start a job and see it through to a successful conclusion. He was an engineer with muck on his hands.

Even at the beginning of the railway age, not every engineer conformed to the stereotype. Men came from a great variety of backgrounds, and advanced by as many different routes. At one end of the spectrum stood stout, stolid George Stephenson, who spoke loudest and best when he spoke through his works rather than his words. Throughout his life he smarted from the verbal battering he received when Alderson, counsel for the canal interest opposing the Liverpool & Manchester Railway Bill, cross-examined him on his surveys. The engineer had been forced to rush the work and rely on untested figures supplied by equally harrassed juniors. He had made mistakes, but now these mistakes had been held up to public ridicule and he had been made to look at best a fool, at worst a dishonest charlatan. It all served to magnify his prejudice against the socially adept, sophisticated 'London men'.

Just such a man was Charles Blacker Vignoles, whose family had come to Ireland as Huguenot refugees. His early career was made in the army according to the conventional route of a gentleman – Sandhurst, followed by a commission in the York Chasseur. He saw active service in the Napoleonic Wars after which he spent two years travelling. He had little prospect of a successful military career: there was a glut of ambitious young officers at the time. So in 1817 he began a new career, in the event an adventurous one, as a surveyor in South Carolina. Back in England in 1824, an experienced surveyor and engineer, he was at once taking part in the world of railway construction. Almost his first job was to resurvey the Liverpool & Manchester line after Stephenson's first survey had been demolished by the opposition. Having done a sound job of work, Vignoles must have hoped for more than he received in reward – a post as Stephenson's assistant, an uncomfortable position for a critic. And Vignoles himself admitted he was no flatterer; he saw Stephenson's faults and his prejudices. In his own words he 'neglected to court Mr S's favours by crying down all other engineers, especially those in London, for though I highly respect his great natural talents, I could not shut my eyes to his deficiencies.' There followed an inevitable parting of the ways. In spite of his quarrel with Stephenson, Vignoles' career culminated in his being elected President of the Institution of Civil Engineers – he was also chief engineer for railways as far apart as England and Mexico.

The backgrounds of the engineers who took railways to the world could not, then, have been more varied; yet all in those days shared something far more important than social difference. Their skills were learned and tested in the hands-on world of muddy cuttings and dripping tunnels. If anyone could be said to typify this breed of engineer it is John Fowler. Fowler followed in his father's steps as a surveyor, but although he had opportunities for further education he left school at sixteen, at his own request, to be taken on as a pupil of J.T. Leather, engineer for the Sheffield Water Works. Later in life he was to declare with a not unreasonable pride: 'Before I was nineteen I was a good engineering leveller, could set out works, and measure them up for certificates to be paid to contractors.' He first came into contact with railways when Stephenson arrived to look at the line for the North Midland Railway that was to link Derby and Leeds. He went for the easy option, choosing the low ground but missing out, much to the indignation of the locals, the thriving town of Sheffield. Fowler was engaged to help look for alternative routes and this brought him into contact with Vignoles. This gives an indication of just how small the world of railway building was in the 1830s. Fowler, not yet out of his teens, was meeting the great men of the age. He was also getting a taste of the rough and tumble of railway life. Not all the gentry wanted railways, or even railway surveyors, anywhere near their properties, and did what they could to obstruct the work. On one occasion Fowler was taking levels when a local landowner's servant firmly placed himself in front of the theodolite, declaring he had the right to stand where he liked on the public road.

On this, one of my stalwart assistants inquired if he also had the right to stand or walk where he pleased on a public road. Unthinkingly the landowner's man admitted that any man had such a right. 'Then', said my man, 'my right is here, and if you obstruct me I shall remove you'; and walking up to the man, he took him in his arms and deposited him in a ditch.

20

An English squire could, as many an engineer found out, prove more intractable than any peasant farmer, and a deal more prickly than any cactus. John Fowler learned his trade on the moors of Yorkshire and the downs of Suffolk and he was to apply his expertise, as eminent Sir John Fowler, in Europe, Africa and Asia.

The chief, or consulting, engineers were the grand panjandrums of the railway world, so grand that some never even set foot in the countries – nor indeed the continents – where their advice was sought. The actual work of surveying, laying out the line and supervising the work went to subordinates, resident engineers and their assistants. Even then, the engineering staff rarely supervised the workforce itself. Once again they used a system developed and refined in the canal age. Work was let out to contractors. The latter provided the everyday tools of the works, which were simple enough – shovel, pick-axe, barrow – and, most importantly, the men. They accepted a price for doing the job and were then responsible for wages. There were many advantages to the railway company. They were able to set fixed-price contracts which, in theory if seldom in practice, should ensure that work remained within budget. They did not have to waste time recruiting labour, and they could disclaim all responsibility for a rowdy, troublesome workforce. At the end of construction they were not left with piles of unwanted tools and materials on their hands: the contractors could use the barrows and shovels on the next job. There were disadvantages: contractors in general had an overriding aim to finish a job quickly, collect the cash and move on, regardless of quality. The engineering staff wanted to see a job well and thoroughly done. It was a source of endless bickering throughout the canal age. A letter written in 1793 by the long-suffering and finally exasperated secretary for the Lancaster Canal to the contractors Pinkerton and Murray, could have been written by any of a score of secretaries to their firm of contractors.

The Com^e are sorry that they have reason to observe that the General tendency of your Management is to get the

21

works hurried on without regard to the convenience of the public, the loss of the land occupiers or the advantage of the Company. You seldom provide the necessary accommodations before you begin to make the Bridges, and in the excavation you place your men in so many various places without either finishing as you proceed or making your fence wall & posts & railing – that the whole Country is laid open to damage. This grievance which has already caused so much trouble and expence is so very obvious & so much owing to your neglect that the Company will no longer suffer it . . . The not fulfilling the promises you make & the want of attention in yourselves, your agents & workmen to the direction of the Company Agent, are evils there is great reason to complain of.

These words could also have been repeated verbatim in the railway age. Yet the system survived, largely because the railway companies considered that the alternative of hiring direct labour was generally a good deal worse, combining inefficient use of basic resources and an often arbitrary system of payment. The contracting system was so well established by the 1820s that it was a source of astonishment to Thomas Telford, when he was asked to report on the progress of the Liverpool & Manchester Railway in 1828, to find that it was not in use. George Stephenson had divided responsibility for construction between his three principal assistants.

Each has 200 day men employed and pay them every fortnight as *Company's* men for laying temporary roads, moving planks, making wheelbarrows, driving piles and, in short, doing *everything* but putting the stuff into the carts and barrows which is done by a set of men which is also under their direction and to whom they pay 3½d per yard to 5s as they think it deserves.

This was seen as an aberration, a curiosity – and not to be repeated.

In practice, the word 'contractor' could be used to describe at one end of the scale a semi-literate workman who had managed to acquire some primitive tools and persuaded a few old mates to work for him, and at the other a financial giant with a capital of millions in cash and a workforce with more men than some European armies. A few of the former in due course achieved the status of the latter. Some of the contractors, such as William Mackenzie who was to play an important role in the construction of European railways, gained early experience on the canals, while others grew and developed with the railway age. Of these, two men were quite outstanding, William Brassey and Morton Peto. On occasion they worked together; at other times separately. Of the two Brassey was probably the more successful, for Peto was to suffer seriously in the great crash that hit the world of banking and finance in 1866, and from which he never recovered. Brassey was hit likewise but managed to rebuild his fortune. According to his biographer, Sir Arthur Helps, Brassey had during his career a total of ninety-seven contracts in Britain for the construction of 2051 miles of railway; his forty-two overseas contracts covered an astonishing 4472 miles of line.

William Brassey's beginnings were modest. His family owned land and farmed at Buerton in Cheshire, and he received a decent education before leaving school at the age of sixteen to be articled to a surveyor, a sound training for his later career. He was perhaps fortunate in being in the right place at the right time. The Holyhead road was being improved by Thomas Telford at the time, and Brassey had the opportunity to work on the survey. His employer, Mr Lawton, also proved a man of some foresight in recognizing the growing importance of Merseyside, and took his protégé into partnership establishing him in a new office in Birkenhead. Brassey was there when George Stephenson came to the area, hunting out good stone for the mighty Sankey viaduct on the Liverpool & Manchester Railway. Young Mr Brassey had the management of just such a quarry and took the engineer along to see it. Stephenson must have been impressed, for he was soon suggesting that railway contracting was a good business to be in. Brassey subsequently put in a bid for the Dutton viaduct on the

London and North Western. His first shot at estimating for a railway viaduct came in too high and was rejected; his second for the Penkridge viaduct hit the target. He won the contract and was fortunate enough to establish a rapport with the engineer for the line, Joseph Locke. It was to be a working partnership that was to prove profitable to both men.

Helps' biography of 1872 has more than a touch of hagiography about it. There is no denying that Brassey was immensely successful: he died in 1870 leaving an estate of over £3 million. It is also clear that he was not only a man with a keen business sense, but that he combined it with generosity of spirit. He was a leader who was not afraid to delegate, once he was certain that trust was justified. A young estimator described how Brassey called him in and went through all his figures with immense precision, but having done so once, did not feel it necessary to do so again. He knew his office staff and appreciated their worth, and he knew his labourers equally well; he was aware that ultimately it was on their muscle-power that his fortune depended. An employer who can gain the affection as well as the respect of a gang of hard-drinking navvies has to be a man of special qualities. The tender-heartedness of William Brassey is praised by Helps: 'At the busiest period of his life he would travel hundreds of miles in order to be at the bedside of a sick or a dying friend, and to give what aid or consolation he could give him.' A copy of the book was sent to the family of William Mackenzie, and a tart note pencilled in the margin declares that he never came anywhere near the sick-bed of his old partner. Edward McKenzie, William's younger brother who was also at the works at the time, was deeply shocked by this oversight and had a number of unflattering things to say about Brassey in his diary. Clearly the event was never forgotten by the McKenzies. It is comforting, after reading a biography such as this, to discover that the hero was not perhaps a paragon of all the virtues.

Morton Peto at the start of his career was more privileged than Brassey. He inherited his father's already prosperous building company, based in East Anglia but undertaking national projects, including the erection of Nelson's Column in Trafalgar Square. He always retained a very strong local interest, promoting dock facilities and rail connections to build up the local port of Lowestoft. Like Brassey his reputation was made on the basis of fair dealing: he delivered what he promised to the railway companies he dealt with around the world, and he treated those who worked for him with equally scrupulous fairness. Although men such as Peto and Brassey made immense fortunes, much of their wealth was in the form of shares and bonds, taken in part payment of a contract. When there was a general collapse in financial confidence and banks were even forced to close their doors, as happened in 1866, their fortunes were seen to consist of almost worthless pieces of paper, while their commitments had to be met in the coin of the realm.

If a railway construction unit was a pyramid with the chief engineer at the apex, then the whole structure rested on a massive base made up of tens of thousands of workers, the navvies. They too had their origin in the canal age; the the name is an abbreviation of 'navigators', referring to the fact that they dug out a navigation. When the canal age began the full-time navvy had not come into existence, and labour was recruited locally. By the 1780s, the Reverend Stebbing Shaw, visiting the works on the Basingstoke Canal was noting that

> The contractor, agreeable to the request of the company of proprietors, gives the preference to all the natives who are desirous of this work, but such is the power of use over nature, that while these industrious poor are by all their efforts incapable of earning a sustenance, those who are brought from similar works, cheerfully obtain a comfortable support.

In other words, the professional navvy had been born. Tramping from one working site to the next, he could outwork any rival. His reputation, for hard living as much as for hard working, was fearsome. No one could match him for strength and stamina, not the rural workers from the fields of England, and certainly not,

25

both in his own estimate and in that of many others, any foreign workers.

So it was that as the railway age began to gather momentum, Britain was established as the one country where every element for achievement was to be found. There were investors keen for new railway schemes in which to place their funds. There were engineers skilled and experienced in the new technology of the modern age of transport, who understood everything from the complex workings of a steam engine to the best method of building a high, stable embankment across a deep valley. There were contractors who could be trusted to understand the engineer's plans and carry them out in earth, brick, stone and iron. And there was a labour force with special skills and strong sinews, ready to tackle any scheme their employers could devise. Small wonder that as men all over the world began to dream of a web of iron rails spreading across their countries, they looked to the British to turn their dreams into reality.

CHAPTER TWO

Europe

The Russians can reasonably claim the honour of being the first to show an interest in British railway building with the visit of the Grand Duke Nicholas to the Middleton Colliery Railway. He was, at any rate, sufficiently impressed to order a model of Matthew Murray's locomotive. When he later became Tsar Nicholas I he made it clear that his enthusiasm for railways was undimmed. It was, indeed, widely rumoured that the Tsar had sent spies to England to report on new industrial processes.

In many ways Russia was the least likely country to dash forward into the railway age. Firstly, it was a land divided, part Asian, part European, with a ruling class that yearned for the sophistication of French culture, but wished to combine it with the absolute rule of a feudal court. Although it was a country that valued science, the arts and industry, it depended economically on peasants and serfs. It also aspired to the new railways before it had even acquired roads that were better than muddy tracks. These filthy winding roads, virtually unusable in the atrocious northern winter, did as much to defeat Napoleon's army as any deed of the Russian army. Nationalists and religious zealots of the Orthodox church feared the new system, while others, like the very pro-Western Prince Viazemsky, mythologized it.

Railroads have already annihilated, and in time shall completely annihilate, old previous means of transportation. Other powers, other steams have already long ago put out

27

the fire of the winged horse, whose weighted hoof has cut off the life-giving flow that has quenched the thirst of so many gracious and poetic generations.

This was a very long way from the realities of railway life among the coalfields of north-east England. But Russia had its pragmatists as well as its dreamers.

In the 1820s, the Cherepanov family was running a factory making machine tools, and they became interested in using steam power. E.A. Cherepanov was despatched to England to investigate how this could be done. He saw a number of machines, and came home confident enough to start building engines at the company's own factory. In 1830 it was proposed that a steam railway should be built from a copper mine at Nizhni i Tagil in the Urals to the factory. As these were only two miles apart it is indicative of the state of the roads that this project was deemed worthwhile. This time it was M.E. Cherepanov's turn to go to England and to inspect the 'road steam engines'. In the 1820s steam engines were so widespread and had already been around for over a century, that no one minded the presence of an inquisitive foreigner. Steam locomotives were a very different matter. Robert Stephenson's works were already beginning to build up an impressive export business, and uninvited visitors were not encouraged. Nevertheless, Cherepanov was able to see locomotives out on the track in normal service, even if he could not watch them being built. He was back home in 1833 confident he could build an engine on the Stephenson model. In fact he was to build two to fit a track laid out to the Russian gauge of 2 arshim 5 vershak, or approximately 5 ft. 5 inches. In 1836 the first train set off on its pioneering run. It may have looked remarkably like a Stephenson engine, but its performance was nowhere near as good. Cherepanov had not been able to get quite close enough to the original for that. For its first genuine line for freight and passenger traffic Russia had after all to turn to Britain for expertise and hardware.

In spite of the British connection, it was an Austrian, Franz Anton von Gestner, who first appeared in Russia with plans for a mainline railway to run from Tsarokoe Selo, home of the Imperial Summer Palace, to St Petersburg. Although the engineer was Austrian, almost everything used on the line came from Britain. Although Russia already had a successful iron industry and could, no doubt, have supplied rails for the line, it was actually cheaper to order rails from Merthyr Tydfil and ship them to Russia than to bring them overland from the Urals. If ever there was an argument for a railway system in Russia then this was it.

A whole variety of orders was sent from Russia to England – everything from turntables to cattle trucks – but by far the most important items were the four locomotives. Two were supplied by the Robert Stephenson works at Newcastle, the other pair came from Timothy Hackworth's works at Shildon on the Stockton & Darlington Railway. The Russians, perhaps realizing that an order specifying a gauge measured in arshim and vershak would pose problems in north-east England, settled instead for a six-foot gauge: a suitably Imperial measure. Later Russian lines were to be built to the more modest gauge of 5 ft. 6 inches.

Timothy Hackworth, having survived the disappointment of the Rainhill Trials, had established a successful locomotive building business. Like so many stories of railway builders in distant lands, there is more than a hint of *Boys Own Paper* heroics in the surviving papers relating to the Russian adventures of the Hackworth family.

The story begins prosaically enough with the first engine, costed out with nice exactness at £1,884 2s. 9¾d., to include the tender. It was a typical product of the Hackworth works of that time, 2-2-2 wheel arrangement, with five feet diameter drive wheels. The somewhat odd feature was the cylinders, which were 17 inches in diameter with a very short 9-inch stroke, a design feature that was to enjoy no more than a temporary vogue. The first engine was despatched in the care of Timothy's seventeen-year-old son John, accompanied by the Shildon foreman George Thompson and a small team of erectors and fitters. John Hackworth's overseas visit was not lacking in incident. He travelled in winter and had to make his way by sleigh from the only open Baltic port to St Petersburg. Young Hackworth recorded nonchalantly – as though such occurrences were commonplace in County Durham – that the whisky in their flasks froze and they were pursued by a pack of wolves. When they arrived they faced the confusing task of trying to instruct the Russians in the mysteries of the steam locomotive. Von Gestner's men were simultaneously working on the track itself. At any one time a conversation might be held in English, Russian, Flemish or German.

The Tsar himself came to see the first trial of the engine, and told John Hackworth of his earlier visit to England. He was very flattering about the new engine, declaring that he 'could not have conceived it possible so radical a change could have been effected within 20 years.'

The locomotive was not, however, without its problems. In the early days of British railways, locomotives were run on coke following a requirement first brought in on the Liverpool & Manchester that locomotives should 'consume their own smoke'. In Russia, coal and wood were tried with poor results: log burning was a particularly spectacular failure, as a Vesuvius of sparks burst out of the chimney, blew back over passengers in open carriages and set their clothes on fire. Hence coke had to be imported from England. A more pressing problem, however, was the cold. On one occasion, the freezing conditions led one of the cylinders to crack. George Thompson simply set off for Moscow, a mere 600 miles away, had a pattern made from which a new cylinder was cast and bored, and then returned to St Petersburg where he fitted the new cylinder. The locomotive was put back to work.

Once the engine had been successfully put through its trials it was ready for public use, but not without an official blessing by the Orthodox church in the presence of the Tsar and his family. Water was collected from a nearby bog and poured into a golden censer, in a ring of a hundred hurdles, where it was sanctified by the immersion of a golden cross. While a choir sang, priests gave their blessings. Then, using a large brush, the holy water was dashed with great vigour in the form of a cross over each wheel of the locomotive and also, inadvertently, over John Hackworth on the footplate. After that, and including prayers for the safe passage of the Tsar and all his family, the new age of passenger transport in Russia was declared open.

As with many countries, Russia only needed help over the first difficult step before using her increasing knowledge and confidence to develop her own rail system. It was not an easy process, particularly the financing of lines. A system was arrived at which was to prove popular in many other parts of the world. The government guaranteed a minimum return on investors' capital – in this case 4 per cent – and with this guarantee the stockbrokers, Harman and Co., were able to raise the money on the London market for the ambitious and expensive line from St Petersburg to Moscow.

In France the position was reversed. The French began railway building on their own account. The innovative engineer Marc Seguin designed a locomotive in 1828 for the Lyons & St Etienne Railway, though even Robert Stephenson & Co. was commissioned to produce it. However, enthusiasm for railways was slow to develop.

As early as 1833 Vignoles was surveying a line that would link London to Paris. That proved too ambitious for financiers to contemplate, so a more modest proposal was put forward for a purely French line from Paris to Dieppe, with a branch line to Rouen. The Minister of Public Instruction, Monsieur Thiers, visited England to look at the new railways, but declared himself horrified at such monstrosities and would do nothing at all to promote railway building in France. The banker, Charles Lafitte, was highly indignant at this lack of interest in the new transport system, and lashed out furiously, decrying the 'dearth of capital, the mistrust of the inhabitants, the charlatanism of speculators'. He recruited the help of an English entrepreneur, Edward Blount, a man of many parts. He was political agent to the Duke of Norfolk, an advocate of reform and, most importantly, a man who had the confidence of financiers of the calibre of Rothschild and Montefiore. In 1839 they approached the French government for help with the London & Southampton Railway. This line

31

was an obvious choice. The route was to depend for much of its traffic on the port of Southampton, and a cross-channel link to a railway at Dieppe was clearly very much in their interests. The French government was to subscribe 28 per cent of the total of £2 million capital and the rest was to be raised equally in London and Paris. The chairman of the company, W.J. Chaplin, one of the directors, William Reed, and the chief engineer Joseph Locke went to France, were satisfied with what they saw of the likely route and it was agreed that work would start on the Paris to Rouen section.

Locke had originally intended to use French contractors and French labour, but French contractors' prices were unreasonably high, so the work was put out to tender in Britain. Thomas Brassey and William Mackenzie put in bids and agreed, probably wisely as neither had experience of working overseas, to combine forces and work as partners.

If Locke was unimpressed by French contractors, Brassey and Mackenzie took an equally poor view of the peasant labour of Normandy. There was an obvious answer, as Joseph Locke explained in his presidential address to the Institution of Civil Engineers, describing the departure of Brassey and Mackenzie for France.

Among the appliances carried by these gentlemen, there were none more striking or important than the navvies themselves. Following in the wake of their masters, when it was known that they had contracted for works in France, these men soon spread over Normandy, where they became objects of interest to the community, not only by the peculiarity of their dress, but by their uncouth size, habits, and manners; which formed so marked a contrast with those of the peasantry of that country. These men were generally employed in the most difficult and laborious work, and by that means earned larger wages than the rest of the men. Discarding the wooden shovels and basket-sized barrows of the Frenchmen, they used the tools which modern art had suggested, and which none but the most expert and robust could wield.

Brassey's enthusiasm for the French venture was, it is said, helped by the fact that Mrs Brassey was fluent in the language, which was more than could be said for most of the British invasion, with its army of 5000 navvies. The British were expected to instruct their French counterparts, and Helps' biography of Brassey contains some illuminating first-hand accounts of how the British set about this task.

They pointed to the earth to be moved, or the wagon to be filled, said the word 'd—n' emphatically, stamped their feet, and somehow or other instructions, thus conveyed, were generally comprehended by the foreigner.

Supervisors and others either made an effort to learn French or were given interpreters.

But among the navvies there grew up a language which could hardly be said to be either French or English; and which, in fact, must have resembled that strange compound (Pigeon English) which is spoken at Hong Kong by the Chinese . . . This composite language had its own forms and grammar; and it seems to have been made use of in other countries besides France; for afterwards there were young Savoyards who became quite skilled in the use of this particular language, and who were employed as cheap interpreters between the sub-contractors and the native workmen . . . On this railway between Paris and Rouen there were no fewer than eleven languages spoken on the works. The British spoke English; the Irish, Erse; the Highlanders, Gaelic; and the Welshmen, Welsh. Then there were French, Germans, Belgians, Dutch, Piedmontese, Spaniards, and Poles — all speaking their own language. There was only one Portuguese.

Language was not the only difference. For example, the British navvy expected decent accommodation, but the Germans 'would put up with a barn, or anything'. Then there was the question of appearance. The well-established navvy was expected to wear the navvy 'uniform' and 'scorned to adopt the habits or the dress of the people he lived amongst.' Pay too separated the native French from the rest. A sub-contractor noted that when work started in 1841 the French were happy, not to say delighted, with the pay they were offered: 'When we went there, a native labourer was paid one shilling a day; but when we began to pay them two francs and a half a day, they thought we were angels from heaven.' The British inevitably earned more, twice as much at the start, simply because they were more skilled. In wagon-filling, it was estimated that an experienced navvy would lift 20 tons of earth to a height of around 6 feet in the course of one day. To watch a well-trained team at work in a cutting was to see physical prowess at its most impressive. One of Brassey's time-keepers wrote,

> I think as fine a spectacle as any man could witness, who is accustomed to look at work, is to see a cutting in full operation, with about twenty wagons being filled, every man at his post, and every man with his shirt open, working in the heat of the day, the gangers looking about, and everything going like clockwork. Such an exhibition of physical power attracted many French gentlemen, who came on to the cuttings at Paris and Rouen, and looking at these English workmen with astonishment, said, '*Mon Dieu! les Anglais, comme ils travaillent!*' Another thing that called forth remark, was the complete silence that prevailed amongst the men. It was a fine sight to see the Englishmen that were there, with their muscular arms and hands hairy and brown.

Another area in which the British excelled was in the skilled and dangerous work of mining tunnels. Conditions were bad: the air was foul, men often worked soaked to the skin and it was no place for the faint-hearted: 'At times you hear alarming creaking noises round you, the earth threatening to cave in and overwhelm the labourers.' It took raw courage to crawl into tunnels where the timbers were already bending under the pressure of the earth and shore up the space while the old supports cracked around you.

British navvies had other less admirable traits. They discovered brandy, and drank it as they did the local wine – with predictable consequences. Pay days were always an excuse for a 'few' bottles to do the rounds. Otherwise, however, the men fitted in at least as well with the life of the French villagers as they had with their English counterparts.

Helps' biography of Brassey gives the broad sweep of the life of railway builders in France in the 1840s. A more detailed picture emerges from the diaries and papers of his partner William Mackenzie and his younger brother, Edward. The two contractors established offices in France and Edward set up house there, bringing his family out to join him. He worked on the Paris to Rouen line right up to its opening, and then promptly went on to start work on the Rouen to Le Havre Railway in 1843.

They faced many problems. It was obviously in their interest, having brought their army over to France, to ensure that it was fully occupied. This was not always easy. Weather in January might make work impossible. On 10 January 1842, Edward noted in his diary: 'Very few men at work, the Frost being so deep into the ground, in the afternoon Rhodes and I went to Mezieres. The men with great difficulty kept at work. Very cold.' In the event, the weather got worse and nothing at all was done until the 17th. When the weather was favourable, work might be held up because the company had not completed the deeds for buying the land.

I left early, Turner with me, for Les Mureaux, met Worthington and a great gang of men being idle for want of possession of land. He went with me into the wood near Epone and pointed out where a small piece of land was got, and we commenced and cut out a gully. I then returned home to breakfast.

Delays could, however, be, a good deal more troublesome. In February 1843 he wrote,

I went to the Poissy end of the works where a gang of men were at work making up part of an embankment at that point, working to every disadvantage not to stop the ballasting from Poissy. This job might have been done six months ago but we were not allowed to break ground at that time.

A rather more common complaint received no more than the laconic jotting: 'Very few men at work being pay Monday.' There was no more success on the Tuesday either.

Pay was a recurring problem. Contractors were not easily persuaded to offer extras no matter what the circumstances: 'A man was killed by a fall this morning in the waggon face east end of Nanty Hill. The men in consequence turned out for more wages but they were not any better for it and went to work on the same terms.'

In general, the Mackenzies knew their own men well, and the diaries are full of entries referring to men like 'old Price' or 'old John Henman', who would come over from England looking for work and be given it straight away. Men appeared who were last seen tipping at 'the Liverpool tunnel', and others who came not on their own but now with a son ready to follow on the navvy trail. There might be the occasional critical comment: 'Some Irish men were very impudent and saucy', or bad work noted: 'culverts built by vagabonds the name Casey & Eagin'. Not that Edward was above criticism himself. William noted in *his* diary for 2 Feb 1842 that the foundations of the bridge at Rosney were in a poor state: 'Edward was told to use hydraulic mortar, but did not, neglected doing so which is very bad work in such situations and very often we suffer in consequence.' This event does not appear in Edward's notes.

On the whole, the brothers got on well together, and with the workforce they had brought with them. They found the French – and the French authorities – a good deal more difficult to cope with. Sometimes the problem was no more than the sort of fracas that could as easily have happened anywhere. A Frenchman hit one of the contracting staff, and when he came to collect his final pay was 'very insolent'. He was sent packing, after which the mayor and a gendarme turned up, rather too late to be of any use. Far more disturbing was a series of events that began when one of the French gangers, Lamours, responsible for paying the labourers, collected 5300 francs for work done, and then absconded, leaving the men unpaid. The next day they turned up demanding their cash, but 'We sent them off'. As far as the contractors were concerned, their deal was with the absent Monsieur Lamours and he had been paid: nothing that happened after that was their concern. The third day of the affair, things grew worse. Brassey appeared on site with Joseph Locke, who was not happy with the quality of the masonry work. Brassey then suggested to Edward Mackenzie that he follow them to Bonnivray. Edward recounts,

> I followed but was stopped by Lamours men, who said they
> must be paid before they would let me go. I was kept 2½
> hours and was released by some Dragoons sent from
> Vernon.

The matter was now referred to the authorities, who decided that the Mackenzies had indeed met their legal obligations, but to keep the peace the men would have to be paid. Edward was disgusted: 'They said this is French law – the people are masters not the magistrates. We had to pay the men 7120 francs – this sum is now to be paid twice.' He was a good deal more cautious a few weeks later when he had to deal with a somewhat suspicious Belgian ganger, Delmier.

> Returned along the line, paid the Belgian and asked his men
> if they were satisfied he would pay them. They all said they
> were. I gave him his money and left them.

History was shortly to repeat itself, and in the most embarrassing circumstances. This time not only were Locke and Brassey at the works on a visit, they had the Minister of Public Works with them: 'Word came through that Delmier men were come to the

37

office. The Belgian had sloped after all the precautions we had taken.' The result was inevitable: the payment had to be made all over again.

Occasionally the contractors were more fortunate. While working on the Orleans railway, Edward heard that a ganger called Simcox had left without paying his men. There was a fair chance he was heading for home, and sure enough he was caught about to catch a coach to Paris. He was hauled back, made to hand over all the money, 1300 francs, and was then sacked on the spot.

Mackenzie had at least his core of British navvies, and this made life a great deal easier than it was for William Lloyd, who had only started his engineering apprenticeship in 1838 and in 1842 found himself on his way to a post as resident engineer on the 'Great Northern of France'. It was all very different from the scene he had left behind in Croydon: 'Then France was French, our bedrooms were not too luxurious, the floors were of red tiles innocent of carpet, water was limited in quantity, and soap was absent from the washstand – this had to be purchased off the chamber-maid.'

He arrived with six navvies to take charge of work at Beaumont, but found there were no men, no tools, no equipment of any kind whatsoever, simply a 'preremptory order' to employ 300 men and start work at once. More in hope than expectation, he put up notices asking local peasants to turn up on the next morning with whatever tools they owned. When he went to the meeting place he found 'a motley crowd of volunteer navvies, numbering more than a hundred, with every species of earth-disturbing implement, and with a perfect collection of wheelbarrows, many of remote antiquity.' He set this makeshift band to work, but was delighted when a gang of Belgian navvies with experience on the railways appeared looking for work. He hired them on the spot – and created a riot. The French did not want Belgian workers. In fact they claimed they would kill any Belgian who as much as picked up a shovel. Lloyd went to talk to the French, but rather than pacifying them, his speech seemed only to make them more irate. One of the English navvies, known as Tom

Breakwater from his having been born on Plymouth breakwater, came up to Lloyd to ask what it was the angry men were shouting. Lloyd explained that they were threatening to throw him in the river, a prospect which Tom Breakwater accepted with equanimity. He coolly remarked, 'Never mind, master, I'll pull you out.' Lloyd had a better scheme. It was, he declared, a King's Fête day, and everyone could have the day off. This was greeted with great enthusiasm. Lloyd, not surprisingly, felt in need of a restorative and popped in to the local inn, where he was cheerily greeted by the ringleaders of the mini-rebellion. He spent the rest of the day drinking the King's health with the men who a few hours before had threatened to drown him. What happened on the next day history does not tell. This little adventure at the beginning of his career did nothing to deter Lloyd, who spent much of his life travelling the world as an itinerant railway builder – as indeed did the laconic Tom Breakwater.

Lloyd's experience was an unusual one. Most French railways appear to have adopted the practice established by Locke and other engineers of leaving the hiring of workmen in the hands of contractors. It was all too easy for a young Englishman, new to the country and not speaking the language, to fall foul of local prejudices. Not that prejudice was limited to French attitudes to the English. Edward Mackenzie, when faced with problems, revealed the typical British reaction to foreigners in his diaries: 'After breakfast went into the town with Tomes – called about the Stabling by appointment, but as usual with the French no appointment was kept.' Or again: 'Paid off Old Blubberhead his store account and took 1000 francs of deductions off his bills and he never made a remark. This is French *honesty*.'

The world of the railway builders can seem to be a very closed one, into which the larger world of politics never impinged. But no sector of French life escaped the events of 1848, the 'Year of Revolutions.' In Paris, the crowds were out on the streets and the barricades were going up. The clamour for reform was turning into a full-scale revolution. To the British in France, events in Paris warranted a diary jotting. What really concerned them was the affect on their workforce, and the problems they faced in

39

getting money from their Parisian bankers to pay wages and bills. The following extracts from Edward Mackenzie's diary give something of the flavour and problems of the times.

24 Feb   Nothing but destruction in the neighbourhood of Paris. Louis Philippe (King) abdicated, all the barriers stopped and the city in open rebellion and Republic proclaimed – less rain afternoon.

26 Feb   Arranged for engine and some horses being sent to Dieppe to finish the work there if the present disturbed state of the Country ceased and things became peaceable.

1 Mar   Some mechanics from Tours came down in the waggon with me to Boulogne. These men are driven away by the Revolutionaries and not allowed to stop.

9 Mar   Some of the bricklayers were standing idle, and said they would go to work no more there, that they were afraid of their lives and that the Frenchmen threw bricks at them last night in the tunnel and told them they must all quit.
          I went through the tunnel, all was quiet and no symtoms [sic] of disorder. Two Gendarmes came up and said they had heard something of the row but that they would take steps to prevent it.

The authorities then agreed to do what they could to prevent the intimidation of the British workers. That problem was, however, replaced by a new one.

12 Mar   Had word from Laffite stating that they had stopped payment and that the Bank would be closed for a time, and he said also the 60,000 francs advised as being sent off for us had not been sent.

The money was sent only for it to be immediately misappropriated.

40

14 March When I got to the office this morning enquired immediately (from a letter just received from Faurin telling me Adams had played me a trick) from James whether the checks I had given him yesterday were cashed. He said no, that Adams had told him the 60,000 francs which had come for us he would take to his own account. Laffite & Co owing him money considered he was first in appropriating our money to pay himself . . . got a statement of all the facts put on paper connected with this rascally transaction.

25 March Paris in a very unsettled and discontented manner, every thief being a King.

His own position was all the time getting steadily worse and he was beginning to pay off the men. Attempts to get more money were constantly frustrated.

19 April We went from here to the Bordeaux railway office, saw Mr du Richmond one of the Directors who said they had no money, and that Government had given notice for all the lines being taken into their own hands.

20 April Told we could not get any more money from the Boulogne Company for construction but that we were to be paid for maintenance 15,000 fr now and the balance the first of May when our upholding would cease.

There was nothing to be done but to ship the wagons and horses back to England and tidy up the business. William Mackenzie drew £400 out of a Liverpool bank to pay the men, and Edward was soon off inspecting a line being built in Belgium. It was to be some time before the Mackenzies were to be back building railways in France.

The financial affairs of the contractor as seen by Edward Mackenzie, preoccupied with the day to day running of a major construction site, were very different from those as seen by the partners, Thomas Brassey and William Mackenzie. William's diary is full of details of new proposals and political manoeuvring. While Edward bustled around the Paris–Rouen–Le Havre network, William was engaged in finding new contracts, as well as settling problems on existing lines. His reputation had won him contracts in France and other parts of Europe, while at the same time other contractors, in France and Belgium, were trying to buy his favour or gain it via threats of political influence. He had already by this time begun work on the Orleans & Bordeaux Railway, but was working from his London office. A diary entry on a visit in January 1845 serves as a reminder that the big contractors needed to be conversant with more than just civil engineering.

17 January   Mr Heddon, Winch, my nephew and I went and called on Mr Wright respecting pattern 1st Class Carriage for Orleans & Bordeaux Railway.

A few days later he received a very different proposition.

29 January   About mid day the Belgian Gentlemen Contractors called on me to propose that I would consent to amalgamate the Bordeaux Contracts with them and Barbier to which proposal I refused to listen – they strongly advised me to do so as sound Policy or the Council of State upset my Contract – They then told me Barbier has sent for them to join him and they were to find Capital and knowledge and experience, none of which he had – they said hitherto they had not seen him. They asked me if I would allow them an interview tomorrow at 12°ck respecting a Railway in Belgium. I complied.

Mackenzie was aware that although the English were a major force in railway building in Europe, their continental associates had the ear of government, as a later entry shows.

13 March Government in my opinion are more disposed to thwarting as much as possible than be honest. Laurent & Luzarch are listened to in everything. The feeling is French use English money and English have no control whatsoever.

It was a situation rife with wheeler-dealers, bribes and the payment of backhanders. Powerful men like Mackenzie and Brassey were in a strong enough position to stand above such mean dealings. Mackenzie's diaries record a meeting with one such easer of ways and opener of palms, Mr Cunningham.

1 April He then said have you plenty of money. I replied no – he then wished to impress on my mind he had worked hard for us with his influence on the Havre line and would be glad of a few Hundred pounds for such service. I flatly declined him. He said in Spain he ought to have some smacks. I would not listen to such proposal, his influence is Humbug.

It was all very well for the Mackenzies of the contracting world to take a high-principled attitude, but the lower echelons of contractors and sub-contractors were constantly on the brink of bankruptcy. Very little had to go awry with a contract for a slim profit to turn into a loss. To ensure that contractors could meet their obligations to workforce and suppliers, it was required that they should deposit money with the railway company as a safeguard. Mackenzie noted that one of the first things he did before starting work on the Orleans, Tours and Bordeaux Railway was to deposit £80,000 with the government. Small contractors often sank all their cash into equipment and prevaricated as long as possible over their deposits. Some prevaricated for so long that they were overtaken by events, with drastic consequences. William Mackenzie visited the Orleans area in January 1843, a journey involving 'the worst roads and worst travelling I ever experienced', and arrived in Nancy to be confronted with just such a situation, involving a minor contractor.

Rennaud was going to shoot himself. It turned out when he took his contract he did not deposit his caution money (£1200) to the Ponts et Chaussées and moreover he had not the means and in the case the said works would again be adjudicated and if let for more money he would have to make good the difference to Government as far as his means would cover. In this state of mind he would come to any terms with me and he had thus far transferred his interests to us. I had him fast but under the circumstances I behaved liberally to him in giving him & Dubeck half the profits allowing us a sum for Cash and Materials but all cash and management wholly and solely to be in McK & Brassey control whatsoever any Mem^n of Agreement that comes O'Neill's claim which I would not at all admit under the circumstance of public adjudication. He brought us interest and the matter was free to us nevertheless I gave him a verbal promise of £100 not to be considered a claim and that his interest had done us any favour whatsoever. His position is wholly and solely the personal interest he professes to have by Deputies, Ministers &c and that he can put us in a Train by connecting ourselves with Rennaud and Dubeck to procure private Contracts from Government that will yield a return of 30 to 40% profit. We of course furnish all the funds and management and manage funds on the Marne and Rhône Canal is the first large job to be obtained. It is 6000 metres in length about 30 miles from Bordeaux. I beg in fear it will be much the same as the canal and turn out that Government would give it to us without either Dubeck's interest or Rennaud's and we could do it for a less figure by not being hampered by these speculators who have nothing to lose and might gain something however I will follow it.

His view of Rennaud was a model of charity compared with his comments on Mr Barry of the Bordeaux Board. He was 'a base double dealing villain' and he told him so to his face.

Reading the day-by-day account of contractors at work in France, such events obviously stand out, but more impressive is the picture that slowly builds up of the steady, relentless advance of a railway and the immense resources that were needed in its construction. On one day one reads of buying bricks in Paris for tunnel lining: the two batches he agreed on came to a total of a million bricks, for which half the cash was put up in advance. At the opposite extreme, negotiations with a local farmer for permission to open a quarry on his land came to a happy conclusion when the deal was struck for 'a case of needles and a pair of English scissors'. William Mackenzie's time was divided between England and France, making deals running into hundreds of thousands of pounds, but he still found time to make regular visits to the works, where he took a minute interest in everything, even-handedly doling out praise and blame. A period in the summer of 1845 shows something of the variety of this life.

23 June   Started a contract with Belgian interests – Bischoffsheam & Oppenheim. Gave sureties – caution money to Belgian govt. 111775.05 fr.

23 July   Looking at the Orleans rly – visited No 3 Ballast pit where a new mechanical excavator was about to be installed. 'Mr Beary the manager must be sent away, he is good for nothing'.

26 July   We found a French Ganger going well. Went to Simcox's platelayers, he had got over the Viaduct and through cutting into the wood and was going on well. I gave his men each one franc for doing so well. We called on an Irish gentleman . . . he promised to render our men assistance for lodgings in the village.

His brother Edward's life was far more routine: daily inspection of the works, estimating work done, dealing with local traders, checking the workshops and puffing to and fro along the completed track on one of the contractor's locomotives. It was a hard life, regularly involving before breakfast what to many would seem like a full day's work.

As time went on and William became ill – he died in 1851 –

Edward took on more and more of the responsibility for the running of the whole concern. The flippant tone of the early diary entries gives way to a new self confidence.

14 July   Carriages got off the line yesterday and that the Directors were in a great fright about it I at once went to see them & Baron de Richemont explained the affair to me as being the fault of the points which in my opinion was not the case and I told him so.

16 July   I met the 9 am train for Poitiers and Charles with me. We left by it taking the letter I have received from the Directors to contradict as much as possible the blame they wished to throw upon us. I got to Poitiers 2 pm and examined all the points &c there as well as every other place along the line and in every instance can show that the blame is in the imperfect state of their rolling stock.

Not everything went smoothly, even for the mightiest of contractors, and Mackenzie and Brassey were confronted by one huge disaster in the collapse of the Barentin viaduct on the Rouen to Le Havre line. It was a massive construction, 100 ft. high and a third of a mile long with twenty-seven arches. In a somewhat self-congratulatory mood William Mackenzie noted in February 1844 that his estimate for the viaduct had been accepted: 'It was competed for by two French gentlemen against us and we came under them, 10 per cent under the lowest and the next 30 per cent and we in reality are 6 per cent too low – our estimate is 2,008,635 Fr.' (approximately £800,000). Was the need to cut costs a contributory factor in the events of two years later? Corners were certainly cut, but the contractors claimed it was none of their doing. Perhaps this was so. It is a thought to bear in mind when reading the generally accepted, rather heroic account of their response to the disaster. The story of Barentin is often quoted as an example of Brassey's stoicism in the face of adversity. Helps, in the biography, at least gives Mackenzie equal billing.

Mr Brassey was very greatly upset by this untoward event; but he and his partner Mr. Mackenzie met the difficulty most manfully. 'The first thing to do,' as they said, 'is to build it up again,' and this they started most strenuously to do; not waiting, as many would have done, whether justly or unjustly, to settle, by litigation or otherwise, upon whom the responsibility and the expense should fall.

Not a day was lost by them in the extraordinary efforts they had to make to secure millions of new bricks, and to provide hydraulic lime, which had to be brought from a distance. Suffice it to say that, by their indomitable energy and determination promptly to repair the evils and by the skill of their agents, they succeeded in rebuilding this huge structure in less than *six months*.

The Mackenzie family copy of the book is annotated: 'This should have been entirely credited to Mr Mackenzie (W). Mr Brassey was not even in France at the time.' William Mackenzie's diary shows this to be a case of misplaced family loyalty. It also gives a very firm opinion of where the fault for the catastrophe lay. His entries for 12 January 1846, when he first heard the news, read,

12 January   Mr Illidge informed me on Saturday last Barentin Viaduct fell to the ground a heap of ruins – fault – Bad Mortar. We told Mr Locke mortar was bad and proposed to use Hydraulic for mortar and bear half the expense of the extra. He said he would allow nothing, but we were at liberty to use it if we pleased. The result is now to be seen.

13 January   Today I met Locke with Mr Brassey. He looked sad and was low in spirit. Afterwards went to Newman's office where I found him engaged in making a plan for reconstructing Barentin viaduct and instead of building as before hollow piers opening

with 4 chimneys 2′ 6″ square is now to be solid and the piers instead of brick arches they propose timber ones.

Mackenzie and Brassey went together to inspect the damage: 'bricks good, mortar infamous', and then went on to the Malaunay viaduct where they 'discovered some very ugly cracks in the piers that is a little alarming.' They had the piers strengthened with the beams. Even so, the French were taking no chances. Before any passenger trains were allowed to use the line, they heaped 3000 tons of earth on the top and left it there for several days. When no cracks appeared, they brought out a goods train of heavily laden wagons and ran that backwards and forwards several times. Only then did they finally declare themselves satisfied.

The Mackenzie-Brassey partnership was one of convenience rather than conviction, and as work came to an end in Normandy they agreed to go their separate ways. The document of October 1850 setting out the details of their separation is fascinating for the light it throws on the huge wealth of the men involved and the extent to which their empires were built in railway share holdings.

Mackenzie took the Orleans to Bordeaux contract and the Pont Audemer iron works, established to provide material for the railways, for which he agreed to pay Brassey £47,000. In return Brassey took on the maintenance contracts for the Paris to Rouen and Rouen, Le Havre and Dieppe Railways for which he paid £4000. There then had to be a division of the spoils: each came away with approximately 3000 shares in French railway companies, mainly the Dieppe line. This reflected the common practice of contractors taking a large proportion of their payment in shares instead of cash. From the general balance sheet, Mackenzie had to pay Brassey £32,053. In all he paid over £80,000 in the final settlement, of which £25,000 was in Great Northern Railway bonds and another £25,000 in North Staffordshire Railway bonds. What emerges is a portrait of rich and powerful men, whose prosperity was almost wholly dependent on the success of the lines they built. Small wonder that they and their counterparts looked as carefully into the profitability of a line as they did into the engineering problems they might have to face.

As work on the first French lines drew to a close, the contractors were busy looking for fresh contracts, and their travels around the continent reinforced their belief that railways were sorely needed. As early as 1845 William Mackenzie had led an expedition to survey proposed lines in Spain. He and his companions set off on 5 April and crossed the Pyrenees in a coach hauled by the unlikely coupling of two bullocks and four mules. By 9 April they reached Castilego. Here they stopped at 'a very miserable inn' where to make matters worse the wine was 'undrinkable'. The next day was certainly no better.

> We started from Castilego, the place most miserable with 6 mules and about 4 inches of snow. The stage about 13 miles 3½ Spanish league. We left at 6 o'clock and were 4 hours getting through the pass and ascending we experienced frost and snow. The roads were very heavy. The postilions and beasts could do no more, they executed their whole strength and power – we gave the men some of our real brandy which caused them to scold the mules more and more. They have a custom of talking constantly to them sometimes praising them, other times all sorts of bad names and at times barking like dogs at them.

They eventually reached Madrid, then travelled on to Barcelona, from where they were able to return to France, a good deal more comfortably, by steamer. Brassey was to join with Mackenzie in one last project that grew out of the Spanish expeditions, the Barcelona & Mataro Railway. He was then to continue in a new partnership with Morton Peto and Edward Betts, building railways throughout Europe.

Railway construction in Europe was not quite the simple matter it sometimes seemed of establishing where a line was needed, assessing likely costs and revenue, setting out to raise the money, then either pushing ahead or dropping the scheme. Many lines were promoted due more to the *amour propre* of local interests than to rational analysis. A great many more were tied to political ambitions. Continental Europe in the early nineteenth century was a patchwork of states large and small, and this pattern was changing all the time. In a world of shifting boundaries and allegiances, railways were seen by many as a unifying force. Among the ambitious politicians who espoused this view was the great advocate of Italian unity, Count Camillo Cavour. He worked assiduously from his base in Piedmont to create a unified Italy. He realized that a nation where citizens of one area could easily move to meet citizens of another had a far greater chance of achieving unity than one where the parts remained in isolation. Railways were to play an essential role in achieving his political dream.

In 1851 Cavour began searching for capital for railway construction, and an obvious first step was to approach one of the most successful railway builders of the age, Thomas Brassey. Negotiations began for establishing a partnership for a line from Turin to Navara; the political element involved a partnership between Cavour's Piedmontese government, the Italian provinces, Brassey and the local people. Three parts of the structure held, but the fourth, the general public of Italy, showed no interest in joining in. Cavour then turned back to Brassey and suggested that the government should put up half and Brassey and his associates the rest. It probably seems more remarkable in retrospect than it did at the time. Yet here was a nation-state engaging in a major project, aimed both at revolutionizing the transport system of the region and encouraging political unity, applying to a private company in a foreign country for half the funding.

If anything shows just how far Thomas Brassey had travelled since his first contract for the Penkridge viaduct, then surely this was it. For the man himself was not even consulted: the decision was taken on his behalf by a partner in the enterprise – and a junior partner at that – Nathan Giles. And even then, there was more to come. The fact that so successful a contractor as Brassey had unhesitatingly put his own money into the scheme was enough to raise confidence. The Piedmontese, who before were reluctant to invest in the project, now began complaining that there were no shares available. Cavour, who had begged Brassey to take shares in the enterprise, was now placed in the somewhat embarrassing position of asking him to sell them again. Brassey agreed, though it proved a loss on his part, for once the line was open handsome dividends of 14 per cent were declared. The Piedmontese, who had been reluctant to risk a penny, were happily reaping high dividends. On the other hand, Brassey had struck a sound bargain, for he was to be very much favoured when other lucrative contracts were being handed out.

Brassey's partner, Nathan Giles, was heavily engaged in the arrangements for building the Lukmanier railway, from Lucarno on Lake Maggiore to join the Union-Suisse Railway at Coire. This was another line actively promoted by Cavour. He approached Brassey who in turn handed the planning back to Giles. His description of the negotiations (quoted in Helps' biography of Brassey) gives at least a hint of the problems faced by anyone attempting to build railways across the complex chequer-board of European states. It begins with Giles' first meeting with Cavour.

I may mention that it was not unusual for Count Cavour to see people in the summer-time at five o'clock in the morning. My appointment was at six o'clock. I waited upon him as appointed. We then discussed the Lukmanier, and we came to an arrangement. I said, 'There are no "surveys" in this matter, or no reliable surveys – they are all made by the people in the country. Will you share part of the expense of a definitive survey?' He replied, 'I do not think, in the present position of matters, it can be done. It is in Switzerland; and the Swiss are so touchy about any interference of a foreign Government, that I think our doing so would have a prejudicial rather than a beneficial effect; but I should be glad if Mr. Brassey can see his way to making them without any assistance from us.' I spoke to Mr. Brassey about it, and the surveys were made in the spring of 1858.

51

The proposal went forward and Brassey agreed to take Cavour over the proposed line, but as inevitably happened from time to time in the busy contractor's life, other circumstances and other lines got in the way – on this occasion it was a line to Cherbourg and the need to be there for the official opening by the Emperor. Cavour was sufficient of a realist to know that mere Counts must give precedence to Emperors. Giles' account of his conversation with Cavour is as eloquent a testimony to the reputation of the English contractor as one can imagine, and goes some way towards explaining why his services were so much in demand. Cavour said,

> I very much regret Mr. Brassey is not here, as I have looked forward to the pleasure of going over the line with him, and thoroughly understanding how he proposes to construct the two sections, and the carriage road over the mountain. I am already acquainted, through M. Sommeiller, that Mr. Brassey thinks it better to make a good tunnel even in fifteen years than a bad one in six years. I think so too; indeed, I shall be disposed to accept whatever Mr. Brassey proposes, as I have full confidence in his opinion. I should like very much to go over the line with him; and if you will inform me when he will be at Coire, I will do my best to return, and accompany him over the line, as I am most anxious to have my lesson from the most experienced contractor in Europe, and so be able to discuss the question *au fond*, and with a full knowledge of the facts.

Brassey was more than just a brilliant organizer, who had built up an organization big enough to tackle the most complex problems, he was also a man who recognized abilities in others and encouraged innovation. As part of the growing network of lines out of Piedmont, a route was proposed into France along the pass of Mont Cenis down the Arc valley to Culoz on the French frontier. It was named the Victor Emmanuel Railway, in honour of the King of Sardinia and presented immense difficulties to its builders. Brassey, Jackson and Henfrey undertook the united survey. That was difficult enough in the rugged mountain terrain, but it came up with the daunting result that a tunnel would have to be forced through the solid rock of Mont Cenis, and it would need to be almost eight miles long. Moreover, the tunnelling techniques then in use on English railways would be of no use here. In Britain it was the usual practice on a long tunnel to sink a number of shafts down from the surface to tunnel level, and then work outward from the foot of each shaft. The headings would then link up to create one continuous bore. Such a method was wholly impractical in the mountains, where the tunnel was to run deep under a lofty Alpine peak – at its greatest depth it lay nearly a mile beneath the summit of Mont Frejus. The only answer was to start at each end and work inwards. This required a very accurate survey to establish the alignment. In all, twenty-four survey points were established by the surveyors as they scrambled around the crags, and the results translated into lines of posts set out by the two entrances. During tunnelling, which commenced from both ends, a constant check was kept by sighting back down the excavations with a telescope. It is very doubtful, even then, if the tunnel could ever have been completed without the invention of a new type of boring machine by Brassey's agent, Thomas Bartlett, who was put in charge of the construction. He invented a pneumatic drill, which hammered away at the rock at the rate of 300 strokes per minute. The compressors were water-powered, and the compressed air produced was used to ventilate the galleries as they were advanced deep into the mountain. Progress was not spectacular: the tunnel was only pushed forward at a rate of half a mile a year, but given the technology available (for instance the fact that nothing more powerful than common black powder was available for blasting), this was in itself a triumph.

At first the tunnel was advanced as a gallery approximately 10 feet square, which was gradually extended to a 26-feet-wide tunnel, with an arched roof rising to a height of 25 feet and brick-lined throughout its length. As the tunnellers dug deeper into the mountain, compressed air alone was no longer enough for ventilation, so a technique was used that would have been familiar to medieval miners. The tunnel was divided by a horizontal brattice, so that air could be drawn into the lower half of the workings and continue on its way out along the upper section. Work was inevitably slow in the early days, as engineers and workmen alike struggled to overcome new problems with new technology. The pace gradually accelerated and the two ends met with commendable exactness on Christmas Day 1870. As a mark of his appreciation of the work put in by Bartlett on the pneumatic drill, Brassey awarded him a bonus of £5000.

It is not possible to give details of all the works undertaken in Europe by Brassey and his associates, but a table at the end of this book (see Appendix) lists his overseas contracts, together with the length of track involved and the partners with whom he co-operated. It shows a grand total of 6598 miles of track laid in Europe, America, Asia and Australia, of which almost 2000 miles were constructed in continental Europe.

Brassey had to be more than a mere contractor, a man brought in when the engineers and promoters had decided what was to be done. He had to be a diplomat, able to speak as an equal to politicians, aristocrats and, when needs be, emperors. Happily he was helped by his own disposition. He was sure of his own abilities, and liked to be judged by his own results; as a consequence he was inclined to judge others by the same standard rather than by whatever titles they might happen to have tagged on to their names. There is a well-known anecdote about Brassey and the honours he received:

Returning from Vienna, Mr. Brassey was waited upon at Meurice's Hotel, Paris, by one of his agents, who arrived in the room at the very moment his travelling servant Isidore was arranging in a little box the Cross of the Iron Crown, which Mr. Brassey had just before received from the Emperor of Austria. Made acquainted with the circumstance, the agent complimented his chief as to the well-merited recognition of his services, &c., and the conversation continued on Foreign Orders generally. Mr. Brassey remarked that, as an Englishman, he did not know what good Crosses were to him; but that he could well imagine how eagerly they were sought after by the subjects of those Governments which gave away Orders in reward for civil services rendered to the State, &c. He added, that in regard to the Cross of the Iron Crown, it had been graciously offered to him by the Emperor of Austria, and there was no alternative but to accept this mark of the Sovereign's appreciation of the part he had taken in the construction of public works, however unworthy he was of such a distinction. 'Have I not other Crosses?' said Mr. Brassey. 'Yes,' said his agent; 'I know of two others, the Legion of Honour of France, and the Chevaliership of Italy. Where are they?' But as this question could not be answered, it was settled that two duplicate crosses should be procured at once (the originals having been mislaid) in order that Mr. Brassey might take them across to Lowndes Square the same evening. 'Mrs. Brassey will be glad to possess all these Crosses.'

He needed to have a cool head and be sure of his own ground when threading the labyrinthine ways of European politics. The negotiations over the Moldavian railway system make up a story in which the patience of Job would have been put to the test. A proposal was put to Brassey in 1858 by Adolphe de Herz of Frankfurt for a line to join the Carl-Ludwig Railway in Austria to Czernowitz on the border and hence through Moldavia to Galatz on the Danube. It was a major undertaking, a 500-mile-long route with an estimated cost of £65 million – an estimate which was highly approximate since no one had yet looked at the ground let alone surveyed it. But engineering problems were as nothing compared with political problems. Piedmont was building up an armed force and Austria was matching the movement, each inevitably claiming, in tones of shocked innocence, that they were only doing so as protection from the other. Soon France, Sardinia and the Papal States were involved and talks gave way to the harsh realities of the battlefield. Railways had to be forgotten until peace finally settled over Europe in 1861. The political situation, however, was still far from clear, so it was decided to forget about the Austrian part of the route for the time being and concentrate on the 300-mile route through Moldavia.

In September 1861, McClean of the engineering partnership, McClean and Stileman, set off to make a survey and reported back in November with a recommendation that the works should be let to Brassey, Peto and Betts for £2,880,000. Guarantees were offered, but as they were dependent on the whole work being completed within five years nothing came of it. A proposal by Brassey and Glyn the bankers that the line be divided up and each section financed separately was turned down. Prince Leo Sapieka, chairman of the Carl-Ludwig railway, asked Brassey for advice. The reply was neat, precise and to the point.

Prince, After full consideration of the Moldavian Railway project, it seems that we are both of opinion that there is a serious defect in it; namely, that it has no junction with your Carl-Ludwig Railway at Lemberg; and I fear you will have considerable difficulty in obtaining the support of the public to an isolated scheme for the Principality of Moldavia.

If a company could be formed for the entire line from Lemberg to Galatz, with the branches to Jassy and Okna, it would, I think, be favourably received; and I venture to suggest that your Highness endeavour to form a combination with Baron Anselm Rothschild and your friends at Vienna for carrying it out.

You will easily be able to form an approximate idea of the capital required; and should my co-operation as contractor be thought desirable, you may consider I will accept one-third of the contract price which may be agreed upon in shares of the company.

Rothschild, however, was to show no interest and another year ticked by. McClean and Stileman made another detailed survey in 1863, and now the government came up with a new concession at better terms, with a guaranteed interest payment and the government to put up a quarter of the capital. Things were beginning to look more hopeful when another contender appeared, the

Spanish banker Marquis Salamanca, who offered to build the whole line without the government paying their quarter share – an offer which, not surprisingly, the government found irresistible. The principality now felt they were in the ideal bargaining position – with the promise of Spanish money and an alternative contractor they would acquire Brassey expertise on far better terms. Unfortunately for their calculations, the British refused to comply, announcing they were all going home and the Moldavians could get on with it. This was far from the amalgamation of Brassey and Salamanca that the Moldavian government had hoped for. Brassey, in his usual blunt manner, told Salamanca that if he would put £500,000 into the scheme, then he, Brassey, would match it. But the Spanish banker was unable to come up with the funds, and another plan collapsed. At this point De Hertz, several years and one war later, reappeared on the scene and was encouraged to approach Brassey yet again. Agreement was finally reached in 1868, ten years after negotiations had first started. Brassey, Peto and Betts had then offered to construct the railway at a rate of £9,600 per mile: now Brassey was being offered the same work at nearly double the price. Even so, he was not offered the whole route, but only 360 out of the original 500 miles. By 1870 Brassey had completed everything for which he was contracted: none of the rest was open. The politicking had produced ten years of delays, a doubling of costs and a result in which the one effective contractor had finished his part of the works, while others who had inveigled their way into the business had achieved nothing.

Political machinations were not the only problems that Brassey had to face in his middle-European railway days. The Lemberg and Czernowitz section of this long cross-European route was to cause him great problems; once again these were political, not engineering problems. Whilst building the line he had to pay his workforce; furthermore having bought up bonds to help finance the building, he had to pay interest on them until the line was completed and the government-guaranteed interest came into force. He held a huge stock of shares, but he needed to see a line open before he could cash in on them; until that point was reached they were so much waste paper. It was a situation where it was absolutely imperative that the line was completed as quickly as possible, and such minor difficulties as a war between Austria and Prussia simply had to be overcome.

In 1866, Victor Ofenheim, Brassey's agent in Austria, was faced with a dilemma. The navvies were toiling away at Lemberg, but the money to pay them was 500 miles away in Vienna, and in between them were the Austrian and Prussian armies, lined up on either side of the track. Ofenheim successfully carried the money as far as the edge of the war zone at Cracow. There he was told that there were no engines of any sort available. He nonetheless found an ageing relic in a shed. All he needed now was a driver. There was an understandable reluctance among engine drivers for this task, but Ofenheim succeeded by offering a huge fee for the dash and promising the driver that if he did chance to get killed, his family would be looked after for the rest of their lives. So off they set, regulator wide open, dashing between the enemy camps so fast that by the time the sentries had registered the fact that there was a train on the line, it was out of reach. The navvies were paid; if they had not had their money they would have simply gone home. Instead they worked on, and the line was opened.

The difficulty involved in getting money to the men in Austria was something of a one-off problem: contractors were not often required to build their lines through war zones. On the Bilbao to Tudela line (described in more detail below), it was a perpetual problem. Although there was no actual war in progress to impede construction, the country was riven by dynastic quarrels. Queen Isabella was still in her teens, and the effective ruler was her mother, Maria Cristina. They were opposed by a very power-ful Carlist faction, supporting the heirs of Charles II who were in control of many areas of public life. Brassey was not the only British railway builder who must have cursed the day he ever signed a contract in Spain. The Bilbao to Tudela railway was to cost far more than it was ever to deliver. For a start there was the problem of paying for the work in a country where paper money was almost unknown, and the rest was, to say the least, a trifle suspect. The secretary to the company gave a graphic account of what this meant in practice:

> The Bank was not in the habit of having large cheques drawn upon it to pay money; for nearly all the merchants kept their cash in safes in their offices, and it was a very debased kind of money, coins composed of half copper and half silver, and very much defaced. You had to take a good many of them on faith. I had to send down fifteen days before the pay day came round, to commence getting the money from the Bank, obtaining perhaps 2,000l. or 3,000l. a day. It was brought to the office, recounted and put into my safe. In that way I accumulated a ton or a ton and a half of money, every month during our busy season. When pay week came, I used to send a carriage or a large coach, drawn by four or six mules, with a couple of civil guards, one on each side, together with one of the clerks from the office, a man to drive, and another a sort of stable man, who went to help them out of their difficulty in case the mules gave any trouble up the hilly country. It was quite an operation to get this money out. I was at the office at six o'clock, and I was always in a state of anxiety until I knew that the money had arrived safely at the end of the journey. More than once the conveyance broke down in the mountains. On one occasion the axle of our carriage broke in half from the weight of the money, and I had to send off two omnibuses to relieve them.

Gradually the locals were persuaded to accept paper money, but that was only one part of the problem solved. One of the sub-contractors on the line was a leader of a Carlist faction with immense local power. The local agent, Mr Tapp, went through the usual procedures of railway work. A contract had been agreed, and on the due date the completed work was measured and the sub-contractor would then be paid what he was due. In the case of a dispute, the matter was to be put to an independent arbitrator. This was not the Carlist way:

He had over 100 men to pay, and Mr. Small offered him the money that was coming to him, according to the measurement, but he would not have it, nor would he let the agent pay the men. He said he would have the money he demanded; and he brought all his men into the town of Orduna, and the men regularly bivouacked round Mr. Small's Office: – they slept in the streets, and stayed there all night, and would not let Mr. Small come out of the Office till he had paid them the money. He attempted to get on his horse to go out – his horses were kept in the house (that is the practice in the houses of Spain); but when he rode out, they pulled him off his horse and pushed him back, and said that he should not go until he had paid them the money. He passed the night in terror, with loaded pistols and guns, expecting that he and his family would be massacred every minute, but he contrived eventually to send his staff-holder to Bilbao on horseback. The man galloped all the way to Bilbao, a distance of twenty-five miles, and went to Mr. Bartlett in the middle of the night, and told him what had happened. Mr. Bartlett immediately got up and went to the military Governor of the town, who immediately sent a detachment up to the place to disperse the men. This Carlist threatened that if Mr. Small did not pay the money, he would kill every person in the house. When he was asked, 'Would you kill a man for that?', he replied, 'Yes, like a fly,' and this coming from such a man who, as I was told, had already killed fourteen men with his own hand, was rather alarming.

When Brassey joined William Locke, Joseph Locke's nephew, on the building of the Barcelona to Mataro line, they had more trouble with the Carlists. This time the latter demanded £1200 from the railway company for their funds, in what can best be described as a form of political protection racket. William ignored their threats, and a week later a bridge was burned down. When that produced no result, a band of around 200 partisans stopped a contractor's train, hoping to discover Locke on board, but when he was not found they settled for ransacking the train instead. Having failed to kidnap Locke, they captured instead a guard, Alexander Flancourt. This time there was no option but to call in the military, who soon tracked the partisans down and the guard escaped in the confusion of the fight. Life for railway builders in Spain was not dull.

A feature of works such as this is that whereas in the early days contractors such as Brassey relied mainly on their own navvy gangs, by the 1860s they were employing local labour. It was obviously a sensible course in many ways, though the hard-won reputation of the British navvy ensured that he kept his title 'Prince of Workers' against all comers. Brassey, who had more opportunities than most to gauge the value of workers from different countries, was able to compare their various qualities. The Italians were perhaps the most idiosyncratic. The Piedmontese came in for fulsome praise. One of Brassey's agents wrote, 'For cutting rock, the right man is a Piedmontese. He will do the work cheaper than an English miner. He is hardy, vigorous, and a stout mountaineer; he lives well, and his muscular development is good' – and he was appreciated as a steady, sober workman. At the opposite end of the scale came the Neapolitans. They would arrive as an entire clan with their 'chieftains'. Perhaps a thousand men and boys would turn up in one group. They built their own settlements of rough huts made of mud and branches and here the old men stayed to look after the cooking, while the rest went to the diggings. Women were left behind in the villages. Nothing would persuade the Neapolitans to take on the heaviest work. They did what they had to do, lived frugally, and after six months' work packed up their pots and pans, gathered their savings together, and headed for home.

The Germans had less endurance than the French, and the Belgians were generally regarded as better than both. The Scandinavians, perhaps unexpectedly, did not share characteristics. Danes, declared Rowan, the agent for Peto, Brassey and Betts, were very steady workers and the sub-contractors were a 'very superior class of men'. Danish labourers worked in their own

way, at their own rate: they started work at 4 o'clock in the morning during the summer and plodded on, not at any great rate,
until 8 o'clock at night. During that time they knocked off for
five breaks at least, each of which lasted half an hour. The Swedes
were 'troublesome', or, to put it bluntly, they drank.

The contractors were also in a good position to assess the
quality of the engineers, and the Englishman, reared in the learn-
as-you-go school of practical experience, took a dim view of the
theorizing Continentals.

The great fault of Danish technical education is the overdo-
ing of it. The young men are kept in school till they are
twenty-five. They come out highly educated; utterly ignorant
of the world, but educated to a tremendous height . . .
  They have been in the habit of applying to one of their
masters for everything, finding out nothing for themselves;
and the consequence is, that they are children, and they
cannot form a judgment. It is the same in the North of
Germany; the great difficulty is, that you cannot get them
to come to a decision. They want always to enquire and to
investigate, and they never come to a result.

It was generally agreed that if the British navvy was the king
of workers, then, in the early days at least, the British engineer
was also internationally acknowledged as king of his profession.
Even on lines where it might have been thought that national
pride would have dictated the choice, the British were often still
preferred. Cherbourg, facing across the Channel towards the old
enemy, Britain, was in the 1850s being fortified as a naval base.
A railway company was set up to build a strategically important
line through to Nantes, and the president was to be the resoun-
dingly entitled Count Chasseloup Laubet. The engineering work,
however, went to Joseph Locke. It was not to be a happy line
for Locke in one sense. Scaffolding collapsed under him while he
was inspecting tunnel workings, leaving him with a fractured knee
and a permanent limp. Perhaps he received some consolation
from the grandeur of the royal opening, attended by Louis

Napoleon and his Empress and by Queen Victoria.

The great engineers were themselves treated like royalty, albeit minor royalty. Belgium was in some ways like Britain: a small country with important mineral resources, a rapidly developing industrial base and the need to link mines, industries and seaports together. When Leopold I came to the throne in 1831, he proved to be an enthusiastic promoter of railways, and had the foresight to see that there was more sense in planning and building the basic network as a rational whole rather than letting it come together in piecemeal fashion. Given the inter-company rivalries, not to mention the gauge wars, that were to plague Britain, his arguments were irrefutable. Leopold turned to the men of the day, George and Robert Stephenson. Robert was to supply Belgium with their first locomotive from his Newcastle works in 1834, and the following year they both went to meet the King to discuss his grand schemes. George Stephenson, his early set-backs on the Liverpool & Manchester now behind him, clearly enjoyed the fêting and the compliments. He wrote home in high good spirits: 'King Leopold stated he was very glad to have the *honour* of my acquaintance. He seemed quite delighted with what had taken place in Belgium about the railways.' To the Belgian people he was a hero, invited to every important official opening and even made a Knight of the Order of Leopold, an honour which was surely never envisaged by the ten-year-old lad who went to work at the local colliery. Robert was to receive the same honour.

George Stephenson's work in Europe was to be limited by ill-health. In 1845 he followed Mackenzie on the difficult journey over the Pyrenees and developed pleurisy. He struggled back to England, and his doctor took 20 ounces of blood from him during the crossing, which he said, not surprisingly, left him 'very weak'. After that he returned to his home, Tapton House, near Chesterfield, where he concentrated on the intriguing problem of trying to grow straight cucumbers. Robert continued to work, and the Newcastle factory was kept busy providing locomotives for railways throughout Europe. The roll-call of railways supplied with Stephenson engines even as early as 1840 is an impressive one: three lines in France, the state railways of Belgium, Austria,

Italy and Russia, and a whole clutch of lines in Germany. Inevitably, countries would soon be building their own locomotives: engines designed for British terrain were by no means always as well suited for topography as varied as the Alps or the great plains of Central Europe, but in the 1840s Stephenson & Co. could proudly claim to be the world's leading manufacturer.

The pre-eminence of the Stephensons in Britain was rapidly challenged by other engineers who in turn found themselves in demand for European schemes. Brunel was Stephenson's great competitor in Britain, pitting his broad gauge against the latter's standard gauge, but in the field of overseas railways, he was at best a half-hearted player. After the completion of the Great Western Railway, his interest began to turn towards steamships and the Atlantic crossing. Nevertheless, he did become involved in railway building in Italy, though from his surviving letters it does not seem to have been much to his taste. Brunel the individualist never took kindly to interference from anyone, least of all government officials. In 1845 he went to Turin with his assistants to survey a line to Genoa, but that was as far as proceedings went. In November he wrote to Count Pollin to explain precisely why he wanted nothing more to do with the line. Problems had begun when two engineers appeared at the office of his assistant, Herschel Babbage, son of an old friend, the mathematician and inventor of the first computer, Charles Babbage. The two men tried to tell Babbage what to do and one of them, Brunel declared, was 'not even of the Sardinian Govt. but a foreigner'. Now this was more than a little provocative on Brunel's part as he must have been aware that by then the area was Piedmont, and its rulers were fired with new-born nationalist fervour. But this was only the start of his complaints. He was just getting up a full head of steam.

> The unexpected difficulties I find to exist by the (to me) extraordinary complicated forms to be gone through, the detailed reports to be made upon each separate piece of work were enough to deter me from proceeding, but these difficulties I felt bound to meet. I do not feel bound to attempt

the impossibility of satisfactorily conducting the work when
the principal & most essential condition of entire confidence
& absence of interference is not carried out.

In spite of this experience, a month later he was accepting the
role of consultant engineer on the Marie Antonie Railway from
Florence to Pistoia and cheerfully proposing that the hapless
Babbage stay on in Italy to oversee the works. He was in – for
Brunel – a remarkably expansive and conciliatory mood at this
time. Back in England, he was experimenting with the disastrous
atmospheric railway out of Exeter. Brunel tentatively proposed
the same system for Italy but added, almost as an afterthought,
that as all the rest of the Italian railway system was to be built
for conventional steam locomotives, it might be as well to fit in.
Quite so! The Italians wisely rejected the atmospheric. Troubles,
however, were soon mounting. In March Brunel wrote to
Babbage:

It is very difficult to send you out positive instructions on
any one point while every thing seems so liable to be reversed
by the deception of others. If arbitrary rules are to be laid
down for the construction of railways which are to overrule all consideration of traffic & which we in this country
consider the great points on which judgement can be exercised – of course such rules can be followed but I would
rather leave such mechanical work as that to others.

He agreed, however, to go on with the work, in spite of the
bizarre notions of the government engineers, who appeared to
doubt the ability of trains to go round corners and wanted only
straight-line routes, even if this entailed steeper gradients, extra
earthworks and routes that failed to go anywhere near towns
along the way: 'I really believe you may as well take the whole
line perfectly straight as I suppose would be preferred by the
Government engineer.' Brunel also proposed using a construction
technique which was proving very successful in south-west
England: building the bridges out of timber. He had offered to

build one as a demonstration, but again the government engineers would have none of it. They wanted iron, and iron they would have, in spite of the huge expense of having everything imported into the country. This meek acquiescence was shortlived and one month later Brunel wrote to F.I. Vanzeller, whose son was working as Babbage's assistant and wished to leave:

> I cannot be surprised at anybody's becoming tired of waiting for 'progress' on Italian business – I am sick of it – and were no English interests involved would decline having anything more to do with them.

He did continue, and was probably the only engineer in Britain who having declared that he did 'not wish to propose rules for Florentine Architects' could then proceed to consign their designs to the dustbin. Florence might boast some of the greatest architecture in the world, but Brunel had his own standards. He advised the Italians on everything from rails to locomotives to stations. He suggested ordering locomotives from the London & South Western and involving the locomotive superintendent in their design, so that he could give his best; though he suggested carriages would be better supplied to the Great Western pattern.

Brunel was not destined to be one of the great railway builders of continental Europe, but that did not stop railway companies writing to him for advice. His answers were invariably forthright and blunt. The French, for instance, wanted to know his views on speed limits. The gist of the answer was simple: speed limits on a well-maintained track should depend on one factor only: how fast the engine could go. On the Great Western Railway, he declared, speeds of 100 km. per hour were by no means uncommon.

> I trust for the sake of the commercial prosperity of France that no restriction will be placed on the speed – public opinion and the interests of the Railway Companies will keep that within safe speeds. The only fear is that the want of competition on your great lines will lead them to be slow; but for the credit of France & French Engineers I trust that

a speed of 32 kilometres will not even be talked of – that you will not allow it to be said all over Europe that your works are so badly constructed that your *maximum* speed is to be considerably below that of the *slowest* Railways in England – and not one half that of the *average* speed on our good railways, and not one third of that which we already attain with many of our Express Trains.

He had one last blow to deliver: 'a line which does not admit generally of a velocity of 40 Kilometres is not fit to open at all as a passenger line.' The correspondence was not continued and the idea of speed limits was quietly dropped.

If Brunel cursed the time spent in Italy, then he would have been apoplectic if faced by the intrigues and manoeuvrings that beset Charles Blacker Vignoles when he went to Wurtemberg, now part of modern Germany. In 1843 the Crown Prince came to Bristol and was taken by Vignoles to see a number of railways, including the Taff Vale. Vignoles noted, somewhat snootily:

Found him less *arrière* [backward] than I expected. Signs of much intelligence, and he evinced a good deal of interest in the objects of his visit.

In September 1843, he set off for Wurtemberg, pausing *en route* to look at various railway sites, including the incline at Liège where the resident engineer, Hudson, showed off the four stationary engines, each of which was rated at 80 horse power. The route from Liège to Verviers was a daunting introduction to European construction problems, for as well as the incline, there were eleven tunnels and sixteen river crossings. At Cologne he met Monsieur Beyser, who had already been working in Wurtemberg for a rival engineer, the German Baron von Bühler. The next part of the journey was by aged river steamer – 'so shaky that I found it impossible to write' – after which he continued by rail to Heidelberg. It was then that he got his first view of the country through which the railway was supposed to pass: it was not very

67

encouraging. Wurtemberg was divided from Baden by a high ridge with no obvious gaps. He continued by road and a week later reached his base at Stuttgart. If the sight of the hills must have been depressing, it could hardly have been any more encouraging to be faced by a deputation of no fewer than seven ministers, ranging from Finance to War, only one of which had anything to do with railways. The scope for political machinations must already have seemed immense, though if Vignoles could have foreseen the devious manoeuvrings that lay ahead, he would have packed his bags and headed back for his bone-shaking river steamer. There was one more official meeting, an audience with the King, and then he got down to serious work.

The beginning was not propitious. First he sat down to inspect the plans drawn up by Bühler: 'Went particularly through the portfolio of working drawings prepared by Mr. B., none of which appeared to be the least use!' Next day he discussed with a Stuttgart councillor the advisability of using English contractors, and then received a deputation of three engineers, Bühler, Köstlin and Etzel. They 'appeared quite staggered at the formidable series of questions I have proposed but I insisted on having them answered.' He also looked at possible sites for Stuttgart station, a subject that was to recur time and again over the coming months and which was destined to become a major source of disagreement. After that it was time to set out and marry up the plans with the actual terrain.

If he was unimpressed by the working drawings, he was even less impressed by the chosen route. The first section was 'up and down both sides of the Fils Valley, which is too absurd; the other an oblique inclined plane with gradient of 1 in 30, which is absurd.' From this double absurdity he went on to Ulm and the Kiesenthal Valley where things were worse – 'preposterous!' The first good news came at the Schüssen valley where he grudgingly admitted there was a 'good line' – or at any rate, it would be, 'with some modifications'. The good view did not last, for he then discovered that in wet weather the Schüssen regularly flooded and the proposed line would in fact be regularly submerged. And

68

so Vignoles went on, grumbling at Bühler's work while looking for better routes of his own.

On a brief return to Stuttgart where Bühler and his friends tried to impress Vignoles with a new type of rail: it 'turned out to be an alteration (for the worse) in the form of rail originally proposed by me in 1830 and which is well known in Germany as the Vignolesche Rail'. Matters were not improved when Bühler took Vignoles to show him a proposed line in the Enz valley. The result was as before: the route was too mountainous and there were too many ravines crossing the line. Vignoles blithely noted, 'Explained all this as genially as I could to the Baron, who took his engineering disappointment very quietly'. This was to say the least a little naïve. Ever since his arrival, Vignoles had been flaying Bühler, Etzel and their colleagues unmercifully: they could hardly be expected to enjoy the experience of being treated as fools in their own backyards. And worse was to come. Vignoles was being urged by another faction to see the King, speak to him 'very freely' and, in short, propose throwing out everything that had been done before and start again with his own designs. This was too much for the German engineers.

Over the next few weeks he was busy drawing up plans and setting out proposals and was told by his supporters that he had the King's support. But there seemed to be an increasingly large number of delays and irritations – including being provided with a translator who spent more time with a bottle in his hand than a pen. He went to see the King at the end of December.

I made a formal complaint of the delays and difficulties that had been thrown in my way; and I also spoke strongly of the folly and absurdity of all that had hitherto been done by the Government engineers . . . I then pressed on the King the necessity for an entire and radical change in the management of the railway concerns . . . The King heard me with the utmost attention and several times addressed me as 'Mon cher Vignoles'!

His detractors continued to throw up obstacles, however. The Minister of War objected to the line passing too close to the cavalry barracks. Vignoles promptly arranged for the building of a wooden mock-up of a colonnade he proposed should screen the barracks. He invited his critics to a viewing and, to his great delight, the King himself appeared and approved the design. On another occasion Vignoles was conspicuously cold-shouldered by the Minister of the Interior at a state ball. Letters in the press attacking him were clearly emanating from the German engineers, but Vignoles declared it was beneath his dignity to reply. In March the King was taken ill and rumours multiplied. Vignoles recorded in horror in his diary: 'It was whispered at the Palace that the King had decided about the Stuttgart station, against my plans, and in favour of ETZEL'S!' Ten days later, the glum news was confirmed: he heard that 'his Majesty's decision and signature were obtained by Madame Stanberrautz, the actress, who had great influence with the King, and who patronised Etzel.' Defeated by an actress! He left for home on 1 April, grumbling of backstairs intrigues and wasted time. He did not, however, come away quite empty-handed. His seven months' work was rewarded with a fee of 2500 guineas and the King made him a present of a gold snuff box, studded with diamonds. In the end, many of his routes were used. After that it must have been a relief to turn to lines where the sole difficulties were such mundane details as mountain ridges, broad rivers and deep ravines.

The port of Santander on Spain's Atlantic coast established a railway, leading south towards the interior, of which the first section of approximately twenty miles had been opened as far as Corrales in 1858. It was not a happy event. The engineer for the line was Alfred Jee, who had worked in England as assistant to Joseph Locke. He was riding on the locomotive when the embankment slipped, the train was derailed and both Jee and his brother were killed. However, the line itself proved a success – sufficiently so for the citizens of Bilbao to have uncomfortable visions of their neighbouring port stealing an increasingly large share of international trade. What Bilbao needed was a railway of its own that would head south for the provincial capital of Rioja, through Logrono, Tudela and into the interior. As anyone who has ever ground along behind a convoy of lorries on the tortuous roads of the region can testify, this is a far from ideal country for road or railway building. Thus a major task faced Vignoles when he was appointed chief engineer for the Bilbao and Tudela Railway.

As we have seen, a feature of many European railway schemes was the raising of finance on the London market, but there was no rush to invest in this line. It was not simply a question of the physical difficulties to be overcome; political uncertainty was an even stronger factor. As a result, the line was promoted in the unlikely surroundings of Cuba. This was not quite as odd as it seems, as there was at the time a thriving maritime trade between Havana and Bilbao. Nevertheless, those who fought shy of involvement in the line were proved wise. Brassey took out a fixed rate contract for the whole of the route through the mountains from Bilbao to Miranda – and lost £200,000 on the deal. He is said to have commented with remarkable *sang froid*, 'Well, we can't always gain; we must lose sometimes and bear our losses patiently.'

Vignoles again, some years after the German fracas, walked into a situation where local Spanish engineers had already produced preliminary plans. The Bilbao and Miranda showed a startling ruling gradient of 1 in 40: this is approximately the same as the notorious Lickey Bank in England, where additional locomotive power was needed for the two-mile run. The Spanish were proposing gradients of this severity as a commonplace on the line. So Vignoles set out to ride for weeks on end through the Cantabrian Pyrenees in search of a better route. His efforts were rewarded, for the new line, though still steep, was reduced to 1 in 66. There is no record of the detailed surveys for the line, but another British engineer, Frederick Cadogan Barron, came to the region in the 1870s to build a fourteen-mile line for the Bilbao Iron Ore Company. He described how, when surveying in the mountains, they ran out a series of base lines and then took cross-sections every 20 metres. By comparing those they were able to

71

select the best line. Measurements were genuinely critical, as Barron reported that alterations of 4 or 5 feet in any direction 'frequently made the difference between a deep cutting and a lofty embankment.' Things could scarcely have been easier for Vignoles and his team. But surveying problems were as nothing in comparison with the actual work of construction.

The first tunnel near Bilbao was especially difficult, as half a mile of it lay through an unstable morass of quicksand-like mud in which massive boulders floated. These had to be supported by masonry columns built above the tunnel arch. Even then the engineers were not always accurate in gauging the forces acting on the arch, and one of the great stones came crashing down completely blocking the whole tunnel. Difficulties were no less severe above ground. The mountainous terrain made it all but impossible to get appropriate building supplies to some sites, so that local stone and earth was simply piled up to create vast embankments as high as a hundred feet. It is a little ironical that one of Vignoles' complaints against Etzel and Bühler had been their absurd plans for building 100-feet-high banks. The line rose steadily to reach a summit 2163 feet above sea level. When complete it gave passengers wonderful views of mountain scenery, culminating in a viaduct that skirts the 700-feet-high Lezama waterfall.

Vignoles was faced with a major problem on the approach to Logrono where the River Ebro ran for two miles along the base of huge overhanging cliffs. To move the railway out of the valley would have involved a wide diversion and a series of steep gradients: the alternative was to move the valley, which is precisely what he decided to do. He would blow up the cliffs and divert the river. He consulted an old friend from his army days, Sir John Burgoyne, who advised excavating a series of shafts and galleries which could then be packed with gunpowder charges. These were then wired up so that they could be fired simultaneously by an electric current. It must have been a spectacular moment as a large chunk of Spanish scenery disappeared in a roar and a cloud of dust. The river deviation was accomplished using a technique first tried out during the construction of a suspension bridge over the Dneiper at Kiev. First a new channel was cut for the river. Then wickerwork 'baskets' were constructed, each 40 ft. by 20 ft. and divided into fifty compartments. These were floated out into the river, loaded with stones and sunk. Gradually they built up to form a huge weir and the Ebro was in that way diverted.

This line typifies the sort of problems with which engineers were faced. They were expected to turn up in a foreign land, often unable to speak the local language. They would either be presented with plans which were of little value or no plans at all, and would then set out into unknown territory as explorers, hunting out a route. Vignoles was one who did his own work. Alternatively a proposal would be put to a famous engineer who would accept the work on behalf of his company or partnership rather than as a project in which he would become personally involved. The actual hard, foot-slogging work was entrusted to an assistant. As the British engineer would be unlikely to know much – if indeed anything at all – about the country to which his surrogate was to be despatched, briefing was likely to be minimal. Few engineers could have had less time to prepare for a task than William Lloyd when he set off for Scandinavia.

When we last met Mr Lloyd he was dealing with angry French workers in 1842. In 1848 he joined Robert Stephenson's office. In 1853 he was told that he was to go to Sweden to survey the country for 700 miles of railway – and he was booked on to a steamer leaving Hull the next day. His briefing by Stephenson's principal engineer Mr Bidder was short, to the point, but not especially helpful: 'Don't go and make a fool of yourself'. He did not make a fool of himself, but he certainly had an adventurous time during the five months allotted for deciding the railway future of Sweden. He travelled up the Trollhätte Canal from Gothenburg, then across Lake Vänern by steamer, but the last part of the journey to Orebro was a good deal more exciting. He clambered into a vehicle which was simply an 'oblong box mounted without springs on four wheels' and the driver, 'fortified with a good pint of fiery spirits' charged off at high speeds over bumpy forest tracks. To help in the survey, he was given a

73

translator and thirty assistants, all military engineers and 'all of whom, with one exception, were either Barons or Counts'. He bought a carriage for his journeys, but still finished up walking much of the way. It was an exhausting task, made particularly dangerous – though Lloyd himself made light of this – by a major cholera epidemic. This was so severe that travel outside Sweden was banned – which did not prevent Lloyd bribing some local fishermen to drop him off on a quiet spot on the Norwegian coast for a visit.

What strikes one time and again is the supreme self-confidence of men such as Lloyd, ready to dash off anywhere in Europe or beyond at a moment's notice and even, in the latter's case, to calmly wander down streets littered with corpses. British engineers were also noted for their diligence and their inventiveness. The story of railway development in Switzerland began with the familiar one of political wrangling. There was a long period of argument between the various cantons lasting from 1836 to 1846 when the Swiss Northern Railway Company finally managed to build fourteen and a half miles of track from Zurich to Baden, but this was not a great success. The new federal constitution of 1848 at least brought bickering to an end, and enabled a railway system to be thought of as a whole, rather than as a series of disconnected short lines. Robert Stephenson was brought over and in 1850 he put forward his proposal for 500 miles of track, which would keep to the river valleys and would link Geneva to Lindau on Lake Constance with a cross line from Basle to Lucerne. His suggestions were largely followed, though the line as built went to the north of Lake Neuchatel instead of the south. Switzerland now had a respectable internal railway system, but the problems presented by the mountain passes had still to be solved. The first practical solution was devised by the engineer, John Barraclough Fell.

Fell was faced with the problem of building a line across the Mont Cenis Pass. The Napoleonic road over the pass zigzagged all the way – and if a road had to zigzag what could a railway track do? The answer was to provide extra traction. The track had a third rail running up the centre, and the locomotive had an extra pair of drive wheels that worked horizontally, gripping either side of the middle rail. The advantage of this system over rack-and-pinion was that on level or moderately graded track the central rail could be omitted and the locomotive could work conventionally. This revolutionary design was given its trials on one of Britain's first railways, the Cromford & High Peak, where the series of inclines were normally worked by stationary engines and cable haulage. The engine that could cope with the Cromford & High Peak Railway had nothing to fear in the Alps.

No doubt countries such as Switzerland and Sweden, with a sound industrial base of their own, could have created a rail network without outside help, but in the early years of rail building it must have seemed a good deal safer to turn to those with proven expertise. It was rare for the British influence to last for long. Once the first routes had been established, the mystique began to fade. There was no magic formula: if a British engineer could turn from designing road bridges to railway bridges, then so could his French or Belgian counterpart. If a British navvy could shift vast quantities of earth so could others given the experience. There were areas such as finance where Britain long maintained a supremacy and in the early nineteenth century the technological lead was also crucial. The London money markets had funds available for investment and those funds were regularly tapped for overseas railway schemes. The great contractors had built up expertise, capital, equipment and a workforce that was never seriously rivalled. But the gap steadily narrowed, and, in time, European engineers moreover began to realize that solutions developed for the particular circumstances found in England or Wales were not always best suited for a country with a different terrain, different climate and where the lines served different interests. Before that position was reached, however, there were few areas of Europe that did not make use of British expertise, cash and muscle.

CHAPTER THREE

The Crimea

It is all too easy to see railway construction as existing in a vacuum, insulated from the turmoil of politics. True, events such as the revolution of 1848 had a major impact on railway construction in Europe, but it was an indirect effect. British engineers and contractors responded to these immense upheavals in the political structure of the continent much as they might to a strike for better pay: they were unwelcome intrusions affecting the smooth workings of their enterprise. The rights and wrongs of the situation were simply not their concern; all they wanted was for difficulties to be resolved so that the really important matter of sending rails snaking across the continent could continue. The Crimea offered something very different: here it was not a case of politics getting in the way of progress, but of the politics determining events. Indeed, it was international politics that sent British navvies to the heart of a war that began as a conflict between Russia and Turkey.

A great deal of the trade between Europe and the Indies still went overland, using the old caravan routes through Turkey and Asia Minor. Turkey in the early nineteenth century was part of the decaying Ottoman empire, which was under threat from the steadily growing might of Russia. Whoever controlled the Black Sea controlled the land route, and the Russians were on the lookout for any excuse to wrest that control from the Turks. The ostensible arguments that precipitated war between Russia and Turkey involved such arcane factors as the ownership of the keys

76

to unlock the Church of the Holy Sepulchre in Bethlehem. In reality, the quarrel was over who should control the territory that had belonged to the enfeebled Ottoman empire. In November 1853, the Russian fleet sailed out of Sevastopol to attack the Turks. It was not so much a battle as a massacre in which the Turkish fleet was annihilated and some 3000 Turkish sailors were killed. There was a flood-tide of horror and revulsion in England and France, although the cynical might declare it was generated more by political than humanitarian interests. The two governments were determined to prevent Russian expansion to the west and were quite prepared to manipulate public opinion to achieve their ends. They were wholly successful. When in March 1854 Britain and France declared war on Russia, very few asked why war was necessary or what the objective was.

Britain had been at peace since the end of the Napoleonic wars, and in the intervening years the nature of the army had changed. No one expected to fight a war in Europe, so it had been given over to ceremonial and display. Regiments vied with each other like birds of paradise to see which could put on the most exotic and colourful display. The ordinary soldiers, poorly paid and badly fed, were no more than mannequins, displaying ever more gorgeous uniforms in ever more immaculate displays. The slightest falling away of standards – a dirty button, a foot placed out of sequence – was greeted with the vicious punishment of the lash. This was the army of popinjays and paupers that was sent to the distant Crimea to fight a real war in which blood would be spilled.

There were early successes as the Anglo-French forces advanced into the Crimean peninsula having defeated the Russians at the battle of the Alma, but they failed to follow up this advantage. In the event the war settled down to a long siege of the Russian fortress of Sevastopol. Nowhere was the deficiency of the British high command more cruelly revealed. Here was an army, ill equipped and ill prepared, camped out on an inhospitable, muddy plain with impossibly long lines of communication. The army had arrived in September, just in time for the freezing winds that would make life a misery and the driving rain and snow that would turn the whole of the surrounding countryside into an all but impassable quagmire. The British army was no longer fighting the Russians: it was fighting cold, starvation and disease. Ships could deliver supplies to the ports, but there was no way of getting them to the besieging army, other than on the aching, bent backs of the men and a few pitiful ponies.

By the autumn of 1854, some 30,000 British soldiers were camped out on the ridge above Sevastopol, their only communication with the outside world just one dirt track which was daily becoming less usable. Henry Clifford, one of the officers at Balaclava, described the conditions in his letters home.

Our next affliction is want of transport for the Army. It is too bad that Government has made no provision in this department. We have, till lately, been entirely dependent upon the Russian ox wagons captured when first we landed and a few Turkish ponies with pack saddles to bring our rations and forage for horses from Balaclava, a distance of about four or five miles. But the cold, want of food, and hard work have killed the oxen and ponies, and the roads are impassable. We now only get a quarter of half rations of pork and biscuit, which is brought up by the few remaining ponies, and we are obliged to send our Chargers to Balaclava for their forage.

A sorry state of affairs for a cavalry officer, but by the December things were even worse.

The roads have been so bad between the Camp and Balaclava we have had great difficulty in providing our siege guns with ammunition, our artillery horses dying three and four a night.

Military opinion was being influenced, as conscientious soldiers such as Sir John Burgoyne spelled out the problems. He wrote to Lord Raglan,

78

To save conveyance of forage, all the cavalry and a large proportion of artillery horses are moved down to Balaklava; still, it is with difficulty that the troops can be kept supplied even with *provisions*. There is a lamentable deficiency of fuel for cookery, and materials for some kind of shelter better than tents are of primary necessity – all, too, before we can attend to getting up heavy guns, shot and shells. You may conceive the state of our men, and how hard are the duties, from the following: Two soldiers (a double sentry) on look-out in our more advanced trench in front of our batteries, were surprised two nights ago *fast asleep* at their posts by a small party of Russians, and bayoneted! a most brutal act. This serious crime, compromising the safety of perhaps thousands, and so derogatory to every military principle, was justified, excused, by the officers on the plea that human nature cannot support the fatigues that the soldiers have to undergo. The reports from commanding officers of regiments and generals are to the same effect. The army is sickly to a grievous extent, and is declining numerically as well as physically.

Had this war been fought in the eighteenth century, then the above would have constituted no more than an internal army debate, but there were outside observers in the Crimea. William Howard Russell of *The Times* sent back his reports which were read by the public at large. He was brief, blunt and angry.

There is nothing to eat, nothing to drink, no roads, no commisariat, no medicine, no clothes, no arrangement; the only thing in abundance is cholera.

The generals may have been powerless, but the cries of misery were not entirely unheard. Morton Peto was by then a Member of Parliament, and he suggested to Palmerston that a railway could be built to link camp and harbour. The idea was eagerly seized upon and on 2 December the Duke of Newcastle wrote to Raglan that Peto and Betts 'have in the handsomest manner undertaken the important work with no other condition than that they shall reap no pecuniary advantage from it.' Peto called on his old associate Brassey who helped organize the whole operation, and between them they wheedled, cajoled and bullied railway companies all over Britain into giving them supplies and equipment. Now all that was needed was the manpower. Peto, Brassey and Betts were absolutely insistent that this was to be a civilian navvy force, answerable solely to the contractors and not subject in any way whatsoever to military discipline.

The organization on the ground went to Peto's chief agent, Beattie, who was the first to arrive in the Crimea with his engineering staff to prepare the way. Colonel Gordon wrote enthusiastically from the camp,

> The civil engineers of the railway have arrived, and we hope soon to see the navvies and the plant. No relief that could be named will be equal to the relief afforded by a railway. Without the railroad I do not see how we can bring up guns and ammunition in sufficient quantities to silence the guns of the enemy.

Back in England Peto and Brassey's faith in their navvies was being more than justified, as the office in London's Waterloo Road was besieged by volunteers; men who had worked in vile conditions around the world and saw no reason to believe the Crimea could offer anything worse. Some were moved by patriotism, others were attracted by the good rate of pay – from 5 shillings to 8 shillings a day – and a six months' contract. In popular mythology, the navvy was a rough, tough, boozy, brawling, immoral threat to decent society. Suddenly, he was a hero. *The Illustrated London News* wrote,

> The men employed in our engineering works have been long known as the very élite of England, as to physical power; broad, muscular, massive fellows, who are scarcely to be matched in Europe. Animated, too, by as ardent a British spirit as beats under any uniform, if ever these men come

to hand-to-hand fighting with the enemy, they will fell them like ninepins. Disciplined and enough of them, they could walk from end to end of the continent.

The navvies were, in reality, neither as wicked as the myths suggested nor as heroic as the popular press would have wished. They were hard men with a hard life, but their preoccupations were no different from those of other workers. There was a delay in the departure of the train taking the men from London to Liverpool, as the navvies queued to sign a paper allowing the contractors to make regular payments to their families while they were away. The first detachment consisted of 500 men: 300 navvies, 100 carpenters, 30 masons, 30 blacksmiths, 12 engine drivers and men from assorted specialist trades. Along with them went three doctors and three scripture readers. The care taken of these workmen was in marked contrast to the conditions imposed on the hapless British soldiers, the first batch of whom, maimed by injury and wracked by illness, was now returning to Britain. Each navvy was fully equipped, and the list of his supplies would have astonished the average soldier. He was given:

1 painted bag
1 painted suit
3 coloured cotton shirts
1 flannel shirt (red)
1 flannel shirt (white)
1 flannel belt
1 pr. moleskin trousers
1 moleskin vest lined with serge
1 fear nought slop [a heavy woollen jacket]
1 pr. long water-proof boots
1 pr. fisherman's boots
1 pr. linsey drawers
1 blue cravat
1 blue worsted cravat
1 pr. leggings
1 pr. boots

1 strap and buckle
1 bed and pillow
1 pr. mittens
1 rug and blanket
1 pr. of blankets
1 woollen coat
1 pr. grey stockings
2 lb. tobacco

The Duke of Newcastle went to see the first embarkation and asked Peto what a collection of tarpaulins was for, and was told that they were for use by the men until wooden huts could be completed. 'What a good thing it would be if some could be sent out for our poor soldiers, who have to sleep on the bare ground!' said the Duke. Peto told him he could get as many as he wanted in two or three days. The Ordnance Department who had completely failed to provide anything in the way of decent accommodation, expressed outraged horror at such 'irregular' proceedings and Peto's offer was refused.

The ships set off, laden with rails, sleepers and stores. It was originally intended to work the line using horses and stationary engines, but locomotives were later to be added to the cargoes leaving England. The ships were held up for days by severe storms in the Bay of Biscay, but the navvies were not going to let a little matter like seasickness affect their way of life. On the stopovers at Gibraltar and Malta they got splendidly, riotously drunk and consequently arrived in the Crimea in fine form. Views of the navvies and the railway they were to build were mixed. Sir John Burgoyne wrote of them as 'fine, manly fellows', but Captain Clifford was a good deal less impressed. In his diary for 8 February 1855 he wrote, 'The Navvies look "unutterable things" at Balaclava, but have set to work at "The Railway" more because it is their nature to do so than anything else. For my part, I wish they would make us a good road, for I have little faith in the proposed Railway.' It took him less than a week to change his mind. On 11 Feb 1855 he wrote, 'I was astonished to see the progress of the Railway in Balaclava on Friday. The navvies in spite of the absence of beefsteaks and "Barkeley & Perkins Entire" work famously, and as I have before mentioned do more work in a day than a Regiment of English Soldiers do in a week.'

Progress was indeed phenomenal. Beattie had been instructed to push ahead as fast as possible, and not to be too particular about the standards of construction – the railway would not, everyone hoped, have to last for very long. As early as 11 February, Sir John Burgoyne was able to write,

> I am happy to say the railway works are progressing. They have a line of rails from the centre of the town to a little way out; from about half a mile farther they will have a very steep incline, and a stationary engine, and, when workable to the top of the heights, will be of vast service.

The one voice not raised in praise of the builders of the Crimean Railway was that of Russell of *The Times*. Many of the men were living in hulks in the harbour and Russell described a fight that broke out and almost became a full-blown riot. What they need, he declared, is a sharp lesson from the Provost Marshal – but that would not happen. The contracts specifically excluded the navvies from martial law. But though he grumbled about the men, he could not deny the speed and efficiency with which they worked. He went off one day to view a part of the besieging forces, to return a day later to find his quarters unrecognizable; where once there had been a walled courtyard, there was now a railway track. And before he had got over that surprise, the whole house was shaken as a somewhat inaccurate lumberjack felled a tree, which landed on the roof and carried away one whole balcony. Perhaps one of the navvies had read his report.

Within ten days of the first landing, track had been laid to the village of Kadikoi and ammunition was being sent by truck, where a fortnight before shot and shell was being passed hand to hand down a line of men. Within seven weeks, the track had reached the 660-foot-high col on the heights above Sevastopol, $4\frac{1}{2}$ miles from the coast. There was a branch line to the Ordnance depot, the Balaclava to Kadikoi line had been doubled and a network of lines lay across the plain, amounting altogether to 39 miles of track. Whatever Russell may have reported, it seems unlikely that men who worked at this rate had too much energy left for fighting between themselves. A splendid example of speed was on show in the building of a bridge across a stream. A pile driver was landed off a supply ship in the afternoon. It was taken that evening to the site in pieces, erected, set to work and within twenty-four hours, the piles were driven, the bridge was complete and the rails had already moved on another hundred yards. The London press as a whole had no doubt as to where praise was due. The *Illustrated London News* wrote in March 1855,

It ought to be consolatory to Mr Carlyle and the mourners over the degeneracy of these latter-days, that there is at least one institution, and that a pre-eminently English one, which, despite climatic drawbacks and all sorts of deteriorating influences, exhibits all its original stamina and pristine healthiness – to wit, the British navvy. Everything we hear and read, from every quarter, testifies to the energetic, skilled, and matured progression of the great undertaking now progressing between Balaclava and the cannon-bristling heights of Sevastopol, and there cannot be a doubt that, when it has reached its terminus, those engaged upon it may safely adopt the motto of their honoured chief, Sir Morton Peto – *Ad Finem Fidelis*.

The line was completed well ahead of schedule. The navvies had worked night and day to complete the supply route for the Army – now it was the Army's turn to use it. The Commissariat at once introduced regulations: no supplies could be sent before 8.00 in the morning or after 5.30 in the evening. The military had been vociferous to praise or damn the navvy army: one would dearly love to have heard the views of the navvy on the gentlemen of the other army, with their petty, bureaucratic rules. Beattie for one had worked ceaselessly once reaching the Crimea only to be injured in an accident on the line. He came home and died, as much from total exhaustion as from physical injury. The army wanted the navvies to stay on to help build new fortifications, but the contractors were insistent that they were there for civil duties only, though they had armed them with pistols just in case the Russians took a different view of their status.

The Crimean railway played a vital role in the war, shifting over a hundred tons of supplies a day up to the troops camped around Sevastopol. Seven months after the first rails were laid, the railways job was completed; in September 1855 the fortress fell. Peto received recognition for his part, and was knighted. The navvies collected their pay and moved on.

There was, however, one other railway engineer who made a contribution. The senseless carnage of the Crimea, exacerbated by the almost criminal incompetence of generals, horrified Isambard Kingdom Brunel. His first practical proposal was for a floating siege gun. This was a quite extraordinary device. The hull, largely submerged, was manoeuvred by steam jets which would allow the gunner to bring the weapon round to bear on the target. The gun itself was set in an armoured hemispherical shield that emerged above the waves. The vessel would be brought to the location in a specially adapted small-screw steamer 'made to open at the bows and its contents floated out ready for action'. Brunel had just created the landing craft. Sir John Burgoyne was an enthusiast for the idea, but then the plans made their way to the Admiralty, a notorious home of reaction and mind-numbing conservatism. Brunel could only write to Burgoyne,

You assume that something has been done or is doing in the matter which I spoke to you about last month – did you not know that it had been brought within the withering influence of the Admiralty and that (of course) therefore, the curtain had dropped upon it and nothing had resulted? It would exercise the intellects of our acutest philosophers to investigate and discover what is the powerful agent which acts upon all matters brought within the range of the mere atmosphere of that department. They have an extraordinary supply of cold water and capacious and heavy extinguishers, but I was

85

prepared for and proof against such coarse offensive measures. But they have an unlimited supply of some *negative* principle which seems to absorb and eliminate everything that approaches them.

When a messenger was later sent to retrieve the model, the Admiralty bureaucrat seemed not to have the slightest idea of what the model was for, and then, at last, he remembered it – 'the duck-shooting thing'.

Brunel's foray into military planning was a failure, but he turned to another aspect of the war. *The Times* reports, in particular, had highlighted the appalling conditions of the Crimea. In the winter of 1854–5 there were 25,000 British troops in the region, and 12,000 of these were in hospital. Those who were sent to the notorious sick quarters of Scutari had little chance of recovery. Frequently, it was not their wounds that were to kill them but disease bred in the filth of the hospital. The bureaucracy sat complacently by while Florence Nightingale alone campaigned for the sick and dying. She saw her main enemy as Sir Benjamin Hawes, Permanent Under Secretary at the War Office. He was 'a dictator, an autocrat, irresponsible to Parliament'. The original immovable object, he was also Brunel's brother-in-law, and in February 1855 the autocrat approached Brunel to ask if he would design a pre-fabricated hospital for the Crimea. Brunel replied immediately: 'This is a matter in which I think I ought to be useful and therefore I need hardly say that my time and my best exertions without any limitations are entirely at the Service of Government.'

He set about designing a hospital complex based on standard units, each one of which would have essentials – a nurses' room, water closets and out-houses. There was to be plenty of space for each patient, and a fan would blow air in for ventilation. There were wash basins, invalid baths, and a wooden trunk drainage system was provided. The majority of buildings were of wood, but metal was used for kitchen, bakehouse and laundry to avoid fire risk. In April, the hospital and staff were shipped off together. Brunel sent strict instructions:

By steamer *Hawk* or *Gertrude* I shall send a derrick and most of the tools, and as each vessel sails you shall hear by post what is in her. You are most fortunate in having exactly the man in Dr Parkes that I should have selected – an enthusiastic, clever, agreeable man, devoted to the object, understanding the plans and works and quite disposed to attach as much importance to the perfection of the building and all those parts I deem most important as to mere doctoring.

The son of the contractor goes with the head foreman, ten carpenters, the foreman of the WC makers and two men who worked on the iron houses and can lay pipes. I am sending a small forge and two carpenter's benches, but you will need assistant carpenters and labourers, fifty to sixty in all . . . I shall have sent you excellent assistants – try and succeed. Do not let *anything induce you to alter the general system and arrangement that I have laid down.*

Throughout the planning, Brunel showed a scrupulous attention for everything from how to lay a floor to the provision of boxes of paper for the WCs. The one thing he could not have foreseen was the total absence of local labour to build the hospital. The gang of eighteen men sent over from Britain had to do it all themselves, and even with such a minute workforce they were able to admit the first patients just seven weeks after work began – a huge compliment to Brunel's planning skills.

Railway engineers and railway builders were among the few who emerged with credit from the sorry mess of the Crimean War. Brunel's hospital saved hundreds of lives, possibly thousands: of the 1500 sick and wounded who passed through the wards only fifty died. Little more than half of the hapless patients who entered the hell-hole of Scutari left it alive. The railway too saved lives, by shortening the miseries of the campaign. The war was a minor affair in railway building terms but it provided ample evidence of what practical men could do in the way of solving technical problems, wherever they might occur. Such talents were needed in good measure as railway building moved out of Europe to the rest of the world.

CHAPTER FOUR

The Americas

North America was the one area outside Europe which was also marching forward into the new industrial age. The Orders of Council of the Napoleonic Wars, ostensibly passed to deny France any commercial traffic, by denying the rights of any merchantman to carry goods to or from any French port or colony, acted against the rapidly growing merchant fleet of North America. When the United States emerged from the War of Independence it was largely an agricultural nation. In order to survive the embargo, the Americans were increasingly forced back on their own resources. Somewhat belatedly, the British Government appreciated its mistake. A Parliamentary commission reported, 'It clearly appears that those manufacturers have been greatly promoted by the interruption of intercourse with this country, and that unless that intercourse be speedily restored, the United States will be able to manufacture for their own consumption.' The comments were already too late: America was set on the road to self-sufficiency. Cotton mills and iron foundries were established, while inventive entrepreneurs such as Eli Whitney and Samuel Colt were establishing a system of manufacture using 'interchangeable parts', which was to form the basis for mass production. The go-ahead republic was never again to rely for long on the Old World of Europe for anything – and railways were no exception.

The first American railways, or railroads to use the local term, developed as in Britain to supplement the canal system. The most bizarre example of a canal and railway combination came on the Pennsylvanian main line canal; designed to link Philadelphia to Pittsburgh, it was begun in 1826. There was an all too obvious barrier in the way of canal construction, the ridge of the Allegheny Mountains which crossed the proposed line and rose to a height of over 2000 feet. The answer was the Portage Railway which crossed the mountains on a series of inclined planes and levels. The inclines were worked by stationary steam engines and the remainder at first by horses and later by locomotives. It was, in a sense, not unlike the Cromford & High Peak Railway in Derbyshire which linked the Peak Forest and Cromford Canals. But the Cromford & High Peak Railway used conventional trucks and carriages for its line: passengers on the Portage Railway went all the way by boat. The packet boats were split into two parts for the rail section and floated on to special wheeled trolleys. They then set off for a 36½-mile journey over the mountains, at the end of which the two halves of the boat were reunited and continued in a more conventional manner afloat. One of the early travellers on the line was Charles Dickens who described the boat as 'a barge with a little house in it, viewed from the outside; and a caravan at a fair viewed from within'. The author was not over impressed by the sleeping arrangements. He 'found suspended on either side of the cabin three long tiers of hanging book-shelves, designed apparently for volumes of the small octavo size. Looking with greater attention at these contrivances (wondering to find such literary preparations in such a place), I descried on each shelf a sort of microscopic sheet and blanket; then I began dimly to comprehend that the passengers were the library, and that they were to be arranged, edge-wise, on these shelves, till morning.' Other canal-railway conjunctions were more conventional.

The canal that was to link the Delaware to the Hudson was built specifically to bring anthracite from the newly discovered coal fields of Pennsylvania. Work began in 1825. It was a fascinating canal, including one remarkable structure, a suspension aqueduct over the Delaware. The workforce was a mixture of German and Irish navvies who did not get on well together, indeed the Irish lived up to their reputation for hard work, hard drinking and hard fighting. One of the engineers John B. Jervis said in an interview with a local paper, 'No canal was ever dug through pleasanter country – no swamps, or muck to contend with – no extremes of weather. But that doesn't mean anything to these club-swinging Irish. I don't know what they've got to fight about. They don't need a reason; they fight just for the hell of fighting.' Nevertheless, they pushed the works ahead at a great rate and by October 1828 over a hundred miles of canal had been opened, including 22 aqueducts and 107 locks. But the last fifteen miles from Dyberry Forks to the collieries was built not as a waterway but as a railroad.

In 1828 Horatio Allen, one of the young engineers on the project, was sent to England to purchase four locomotives from Robert Stephenson. In the event, he bought just one Stephenson locomotive and three from Foster and Rastrick of Stourbridge. The latter were somewhat primitive, very little different from the old *Puffing Billy* design, but it was one of these, the *Stourbridge Lion*, that was to haul the first train over American tracks. It was a lumbering giant, weighing in at 8 tons, twice the weight the railroad engineers had allowed for when building the track. Mechanically it was primitive, its vertical cylinders working a pair of beams with connecting rods driving straight down on to the rear wheels which were linked with the front wheels in an 0-4-0 arrangement. The combination of the large weight and the 'hammer-blow' effect from the vertical cylinders provided a strenuous test of the simple track. The engineer who purchased it, Horatio Allen, now volunteered to put it through its paces. He set off with the sublime confidence of the young and ignorant.

I had never run a locomotive nor any other engine before. But on August 9th 1829, I ran that locomotive three miles and back to the place of starting, and being without experience and without a brakeman, I stopped the locomotive on its return at the place of starting.

The line of road was straight for about 600 feet, being parallel with the canal, then across Lackawaxen Creek on trestle-work about 30 ft. above the creek, and from the curve

90

extending in a line nearly straight into the woods of Pennsylvania.

When the steam was of right pressure . . . I took my position on the platform of the locomotive alone, and with my hand on the throttle-valve, said 'if there is any danger in this ride, it is not necessary that more than one should be subjected to it.'

The locomotive having no train behind it answered at once to the movement of the valve; soon the straight line was run over, the curve (and trestle) was reached and passed before there was time to think . . . and soon I was out of sight in the three miles' ride alone in the woods of Pennsylvania.

If it all seemed very satisfactory to Allen it looked a good deal less so to the spectators who had seen the simple wooden bridge over the creek sway and heard its timbers moan as the locomotive passed across. An examination of the track showed that a number of sections of rail were cracked and broken: it was Penydarren all over again, and the result was much the same. The *Stourbridge Lion* had roared twice, but now it was driven off into a shed and left to rot. America's first steam railway experiment had not been a resounding success. It was, however, no time at all before steam was again given an outing. The Baltimore and Ohio Railway was opened in 1830 using horses at first for both freight and passenger traffic, but soon turning to the locomotive. There were to be no British imports here, however; instead a local man, Peter Cooper, designed a curious little engine, aptly named *Tom Thumb*, a very lightweight affair with a vertical boiler, very reminiscent of *Novelty*, the unsuccessful finalist at Rainhill. It weighed a mere ton, and a contemporary print shows it racing against a horse-drawn rail bus, with a number of top-hatted gentlemen actually riding on the locomotive itself. It worked but it can hardly have worked well since the company went on to experiment with sails as an alternative to steam. At much the same time, Edward L. Miller was trying out another American designed and built locomotive, the *Best Friend*, on the South Carolina Railway. It rattled along at a very respectable speed of around 20 m.p.h. with five coaches. What is significant about these American locomotives, however, is not their performance, but the fact that they owed so little to the pioneering design technology of Britain. True, Robert Stephenson was supplying a few locomotives to American lines, but local engineers were posting notice that they were intending to go their own way in all aspects of railway construction – track, locomotives and rolling stock. The British, perhaps on the defensive, were inclined to be snooty about the American system. Daniel Gooch, the famous locomotive designer of Brunel's Great Western, took a train from New York to Niagara Falls in 1860 and was not impressed.

> Railway travelling in America is wretched; their republican notions of having only one class makes your company very mixed, and the carriages being all large open saloons with a door at each end and passage down the middle, prevents you having the slightest privacy even if you were a good large party of your own. The roads are dusty and the use of wood for fuel sends a quantity of charcoal into your carriage, mixed with the dust, so that when you have travelled all day you are as black as a sweep.

He complained that during the journey he was reading a book and the man behind not only started reading it but complained that Gooch was turning the pages too quickly. Gooch, with an air of hauteur that one can all too easily imagine, handed the book over without a word. But then, there was nothing about America that Gooch *did* like.

> I think I was never so entirely glad of any thing as I was when I felt, on that day, that our ship's head was turned towards England and I was quit of America.

Gooch was eyeing the American railroads in the light of his own experience, and found them wanting. He did not seem to appreciate that what suited the GWR did not necessarily suit a young country, still advancing its frontiers. The US system was to build up in a way that suited the railways of a continent, and it was to have a profound affect on all railway development in both North and South America. The surprise, in retrospect, is not that the local American experience was so crucial to development, but that anyone else got a look in at all. If there was to be a strong British influence it would logically be felt north of the 49th parallel in Canada.

Canada was both like its southern neighbour and very different. It was similar in that it was a vast territory, much of it unexplored and only a small part settled. It was dissimilar in that there had been no revolution, and the country was still tied to Europe. If these were the only differences then railway building could have gone ahead at a reasonable pace. They were not. To put the story in context needs a brief resumé of the country's history.

British and French were casting their nets off Labrador and Newfoundland as early as the sixteenth century and soon traders were making their way up the St Lawrence to deal in furs with the Indians. The peaceful trading days were short-lived as the traders pushed on aggressively into Indian territory and there were wars with the Iroquois and the Huron. In the seventeenth century the French established the Compagnie des Habitants on the St Lawrence, a base which was to develop into the city of Quebec, and from there they traded ever further west. These free ranging 'voyageurs' were the first to call themselves Canadians. One of the old voyageurs told of his old way of life with great enthusiasm:

> I have had twelve wives in the country, and was once possessed of fifty horses and six running dogs. I beat all Indians at a race, and no white man passed me in the chase . . . Huzza, huzza pour le pays sauvage.

The British were altogether more sedate, but a good deal more wide-sweeping in their claims. The Company of Adventurers of England Trading into Hudson Bay coolly laid claim to the whole drainage basin of Hudson Bay, a mere million and a half square

93

miles. The static English, snubbing the native Canadian Indians, formed a marked contrast with the free-ranging French. When conflict came, however, it was precipitated by war in Europe rather than any local difficulties, although the end result was the same. Quebec fell and the French Canadians found themselves under English rule. There was a continuous move westward. On 22 July 1793, Alexander Mackenzie was able to write on a rock that he was looking down on the Pacific Ocean. Other explorers such as Fraser of Fraser Canyon and David Thompson helped establish trade routes to the west. But these still depended on rafts and canoes and pack animals. The main centres of settlement remained in the east, divided between Upper and Lower Canada. There were local elected legislatures and an imposed overruling council appointed by the Crown in London. There was a population divided among the French settlers and their descendants, English, Welsh and, increasingly, Scots and Irish – the latter driven from their old homes by poverty. Added to these was a sizeable minority who had come north after supporting the losing side in the American War of Independence. Canada was partly settled, partly wild, partly self-governing, partly controlled as a colony and its thinly spread population was a mixture of often antagonistic nationalities. It was not a recipe for getting things done in a hurry. The slow and muddled start to railway building grew out of this confused background.

In some ways, the early history of Canadian transport was very like that of the USA: navigable rivers were the key that linked the settlements together, but it was the natural wealth of the forests that drew settlers to a region in the first place. Thomas Need, writing on the Canadian economy in 1830 put it neatly:

The erection of a sawmill is the first event in the formation of a settlement in the bush. It induces others to come to the neighbourhood since it offers the facilities of building timbers. Thereafter some bold man is persuaded to erect a grist mill. A store is opened, a tavern is licensed and a village has sprung up in the heart of the forest.

94

These communities created rough roads down to the nearest navigable river and a system of canals, log flumes and chutes to move the timber. Winter brought everything to a halt. Thomas Coltrim Keefer, an early protagonist for railway construction, painted a dramatic picture of the frozen land:

Old winter is once more upon us and our inland seas are 'dreary and inhospitable wastes' to the merchant and to the traveller. Our rivers are sealed fountains and an embargo which no human power can remove is laid on all our ports . . . the animation of business is suspended, the lifeblood of commerce is curdled and stagnant in the St Lawrence, the great aorta of the north.

Even in summer transport was problematical. There had been advances from the age of the canoe: the first steam boat had puffed its way down the St Lawrence in 1809, powered by a Boulton and Watt engine, to be followed by a second on the Ottawa River, a year later. The rivers were, however, not navigable throughout their lengths and there were long portages where goods had to be carried round rapids and shallows by man, pack animal or cart. River routes were also notably devious. Traffic from New York to Montreal, for example, went up the Hudson River, through Lake Champlain into the Richelieu River to the St Lawrence at Sarel, and then on a last leg of 40 miles up the St Lawrence to Montreal. Yet overland the route from the Richelieu to St Johns, opposite Montreal, was only 14½ miles – a total saving of 90 miles of river travel. Here was an obvious case for a railway, and the land was flat as could be, presenting no problems of construction. But when it came to framing the Bill for the Champlain and St Lawrence Railway, the legislators took their job very seriously. There were innumerable clauses, one of which contained a sentence of 1453 words! If written out on a strip it would have stretched nearly 50 yards down the tracks. The Canadian businessmen who had shouted loud and long for the railway had the satisfaction of seeing the Bill passed in 1832. When it came to paying for the line, however, they became rather quiet and the money was not raised until 1834 when work finally got under way.

This was an American-Canadian enterprise, and it seemed sensible to employ American engineers to construct the line. However, it was to tried-and-trusted Robert Stephenson of Newcastle that they went for the first locomotive. Here two traditions clashed. James Hodges, who left England to work on Canadian railways, described the American system of building as one where economy ruled. 'With this object in view, timber is universally substituted for the more costly materials made use of in this country. Tressel bridges take the place of stone viaducts, and, in places in which in this country you would see a solid embankment, in America a light structure is often substituted.' He might have added that American practice did not call for the well-levelled, well-ballasted track that was *de rigeur* in Britain. Stephenson sent over one of his 0-4-0 Samson class locomotives which on 21 July 1836 rocked and rolled its way down the lumpy track. The rigid frame designed for smooth British track was far from suitable for the new circumstances it was now meeting. The first steam railway in Canada was not an immediate success, and for a short while horses had to be brought in for haulage. The clash between British and American practice would occur again.

The next portage railway also featured Montreal. The city had grown up at the point where the river navigation had ended at the Lachine Rapids which dropped the river down 46 feet from Lake St Louis. They had been bypassed in the eighteenth century by a coach route and in 1825 by a canal. Now a Scots-Canadian, James Ferrier, was to promote a railway. Perhaps encouraged by lingering loyalties to the old country he brought over Alexander Miller, Chief Engineer of the Dundee & Arbroath Railway, to survey the route in 1845. He followed the line of a stream the Petit Lac St Pierre which meandered harmlessly until it spread out to form a wide area of marsh near Recollect Gate. Miller decided that spoil excavated from the nearby Lachine Canal would do admirably to fill the bog. In the event thousands of cartloads of earth and stone were needed, reinforced by extensive piling, to produce a solid strip along which track could be laid. Even so it remained a perilous place, as was dramatically illustrated in an accident of 1855. A locomotive jumped the rails, landed in the bog and slowly and inexorably vanished from sight. The line was opened in 1847 with two American locomotives, but in 1848 two new engines arrived from Scotland with 72-inch drive wheels that provided new power. Fired by patriotic pride, Miller himself took the regulator on the inaugural run and the little train dashed off to reach the terminus 7½ miles away in just 11 minutes, at an average speed of 45 miles an hour. The passengers were terrified and at first demanded to be taken back by road. Miller pacified them by promising to behave himself on the return journey. They reluctantly agreed, and *nine* minutes later they were back at the start.

The route west from Montreal was via the Ottawa and Mattawa rivers, which had involved the old canoeing voyageurs in forty-seven major portages along the way, though this number was later cut by canal building. A number of portage lines were built, and as they were seen simply as links between steamer piers, there was no need for them to be consistent, so that the Carillan and Grenville was built as a broad gauge, while the little line bypassing the Chat falls was only 3 ft. gauge. One portage line started out with pretensions to become something altogether grander. The Montreal & Bytown Railway was intended to be part of a mainline route from Montreal up the Ottawa valley to Bytown, later renamed Ottawa, 100 miles of main line, with 23 miles of tramway feeders. When work began in 1853 the contract for building went to an Englishman, James Sykes of Sheffield, who brought in the brothers William, Samuel and Charles de Bergue of Manchester to help. The sensible decision was taken to begin on a short portage section, from Carillon to Grenville, which would bring in traffic from the steamer trade as soon as it was opened. When that was successfully completed Sykes returned to England confident that he could raise the capital to fund the line. His confidence was well founded and when he boarded ship he had £50,000 in cash with him. Then disaster struck: the ship foundered and James Sykes and the funds were lost. The company back in Canada was now in debt, but when it was put up

97

for sale it only fetched $21,200. In 1854 a single locomotive was bought to be joined by a Birkenhead locomotive in 1858. And that was to be the last purchase of locomotives, or indeed very much else, that the company was ever to make. Up and down they chugged between the two piers, until the steamers no longer ran and nobody wanted the now antiquated service. In 1910 after more than half a century of continuous use, the two veteran engines were finally retired.

The history of the portage railways was full of similar stories of lack of funds, lack of equipment or both. Even the few non-portage lines that were attempted came to grief as well. A route was planned to run south from Bytown (Ottawa) to the American border at Prescott, where it was to link with the US line, the Ogdensburgh & Lake Champlain Railroad. Work began in 1851 and the going was not difficult, though the way did lie through uncharted woodland and scrub. Rails were ordered from South Wales and shipped across the Atlantic, but in the event there was not enough of them and no cash to buy more so the line was completed using wooden rails with an iron strip tacked on the top – which would have been quite acceptable in the 1750s but was decidedly odd in the 1850s. Over this flimsy structure the first train duly ran.

There was one lonely outpost of railway building in Nova Scotia where a line was built to serve the local coal mines. This line would certainly have seemed familiar to anyone visiting Canada from the north-east of England. It was begun as a tramway running from the pits to the East River of Picton. In 1834, when trade was increasing, it was decided to establish a new wharf and build a railway to be worked by locomotives. A local man, Peter Crerar, who had come to Nova Scotia from Scotland as a schoolteacher in 1817, agreed to try a preliminary survey and the plans were duly sent off to the Railway Board in England. Back came a letter: 'What need is there of our sending you an engineer when you have Mr Crerar in the County? Let him supervise the construction.' And so he did. H.S.Poole of the Canadian Society of Civil Engineers was later to write a report on the plans, in which he confirmed the sound quality of the survey work. The line was built in awkward hilly country, yet the steepest gradient was 1 in 360, and although a good deal of cutting was involved to achieve it, no curve was more than a 4° radius. The hypothetical English visitor would have been equally at home with the three locomotives that opened the service. They were sent from Shildon by Timothy Hackworth and were typical of his work at that time. What makes them seem so odd to modern eyes is the return-flue boiler, as used in the famous Rainhill locomotive, *Sans Pareil*. The rest of the manufacturers had moved over to the modern multi-tube boiler, but Hackworth still had his one giant tube bent round in a U-shape. This meant that the grate was next to the chimney, so that the driver stood on his platform at the back of the engine, while the fireman stood at the front – which can hardly have been very good for communication. The sanding system was what we would now call 'low-tech'. Each end of the loco had a bucket of sand and the driver would throw out a handful if the engine needed to go forward, and the fireman performed the task when going in reverse. The driver of the first engine to be used, *Samson*, was an Englishman who had helped to build it in Durham, George Davidson. And he stayed on driving it right up to 1882. The old engine was rescued from the scrap heap and given a place of honour at the great Chicago Exhibition of 1893.

The early years of railway building in Canada were entirely piecemeal and notably lethargic. In 1850 Britain had 6621 miles of track, but had already been overtaken by the USA with 9021: Canada could master a paltry 68 miles. There were reasons, some of them political – the Province of Canada was not formed until 1841 which delayed development as railway promoters were faced with a variety of different authorities. Then there was the problem created by the fact that so many Canadian settlements lay very close to the American border. St Andrews in Nova Scotia promoted a 250-mile-line to Quebec, a charter was granted and in 1836 the British Government promised a subsidy. But the line ran through Maine, an area being disputed by the British and American governments: the US formally objected to the line, and the scheme collapsed. It did not, however, dampen Nova Scotian enthusiasm for railway promotion. Joseph Howe was a man of vision who saw a railway from Nova Scotia as an essential extension of the transatlantic steamer trade – much as Brunel had seen his steamships extending the Great Western Railway from Bristol to America. Howe, with what was soon to appear characteristic optimism, named the proposed company the 'European & North American Railway'. Knowing that he would never raise the necessary funds in Canada, he set off for England where the authorities showed not the least interest in his schemes and sent him packing, or so they imagined. They had underestimated Howe: if government would not listen, then he would appeal directly to the people. He held a series of public meetings in which he stressed the advantages to Britain of a soundly based immigrant route and a route out for Britain's manufactured exports which would be balanced by the outgoings from the cornucopia of Canada's rich farmlands. He was an outstanding orator and a press report of the time described his 'lucid reasoning, startling facts, profound political philosophy and forcible eloquence'. His political philosophy was certainly unusual for the time: he wanted the government to own and run the railways; what is more he thought that railways, like roads, should be free for all. 'Government ownership', he argued 'would keep down the rates and would save the people from the private greed which is at the time so manifest in the conduct of English lives.' While the government of Victorian England was unlikely to listen to such 'dangerous' doctrines, they were at least forced, by public opinion, to take the European & North American Railway seriously. In 1851 they agreed to guarantee a loan.

Howe had scarcely time to congratulate himself on a job well done before fresh problems appeared. A faction in New Brunswick still wanted a through-route that would include a section of the USA, as opposed to the northern, more Canadian line, favoured by Howe. There was a great deal more wrangling before an unfortunate compromise was reached. The new Brunswickians, at that time still detached from Eastern Canada, were to build their own line at their own expense: the Canadian provinces were to be responsible for their own individual sections. So there were to be provincial railways paid for by local government with the backing of the imperial government, whose only link would be via a private railway which might – or might not – be built in a neighbouring country. It was also a remarkably ambitious project, calling for the construction of 1400 miles of track through difficult country. How this bizarre project would have fared if work had begun, we shall never know, for other characters joined in who were to change the plot of the story.

Among the advocates of the European & North American Railway was Sir Francis Hicks, a senior minister in the Canadian government. In 1852 he met William Jackson of the great contracting company Jackson, Brassey, Peto and Betts who knew something of the scheme for Howe had already put his plans to Sir Morton Peto. The emphasis now shifted back from public financing to private money. The bankers Baring Brothers and Glyn Mills made it known that funds were available for railway construction, while at the same time the contractors offered to build the entire line. If ever there was evidence of the power and scale of operations of the great contractors then here it was: their terms were simple, but staggering in their magnitude. The government was to pay half the costs and for the other half Jackson, Brassey, Peto and Betts would accept a grant of six million acres of crown land and an annual payment by the railway company of £100,000 for twenty years. There now followed a long period of wrangling. There were local interests pursuing local ends, and a strong and growing groundswell in favour of a major – the major – Canadian Railway being built by Canadians, not by British interests, however eminent. In the clamour of argument, the grand vision of a main line sweeping majestically across Canada was lost. All was fragmented, and what emerged at the end was a line split in two: the Grand Trunk Railway of Canada, and the Grand Trunk Railway of East Canada. In the event the Grand Trunk was to be promoted in Britain with funds coming from Baring Brothers, Glyn Mills and Peto and his associates and other funds were supplied by the Canadian Government and Canadian shareholders. Of the 900 miles of railway to be built, the Peto consortium was to be responsible for 300. Standards were set high. This was to be, in the official language of the Charter,

101

a first-class single-track railway, with the foundations of all the large structures designed for double track, up to the earth level, and to be superior to any Canadian or American railway now known or used, and equal to the first-class English railways.

This insistence on excellence was not the result of careful thinking about the type of railway best suited to the terrain, but was intended to silence critics. Local interests were pandered to, so that not only was the line being built to join up with the still non-existent New Brunswick route but there was also to be an extension to Trois Pistoles on the south bank of the St Lawrence and the plans included what would inevitably prove an expensive river crossing at Montreal. All this was being justified by profit assessments that seemed to owe more to optimistic crystal ball gazing than to rational analysis. A major railway system that should have been considered as a long-term involvement was being promoted in terms of short-term gains. It was attracting the get-rich-quick speculators who had been such a prominent force in British construction – a group that was quick to invest funds – and just as quick to withdraw them. It was not a good beginning.

The English contractors were responsible for the line from Toronto to Quebec, and things went wrong almost from the start. The surveying team travelled on horseback to select the line, and controversy soon arose. It was in the contractors' interest to make the line as cheaply as possible; it was in local community interest for it to reach as many towns as possible. The selected route included some heavy gradients and missed some towns along the way by several miles. The contractors' argument was that this saved the huge expense of cuttings and embankments. Local people replied that cuttings and embankments had been allowed for in the estimates, so could they have their line please? Sometimes the contractors won, sometimes the locals triumphed as at Port Hope where the rails were brought to the town on a viaduct across the river.

The early work of laying rough track for contractors' trains

102

went largely to Canadian sub-contractors, but skilled men –
masons, quarrymen, engine drivers and fitters – were brought
out from England at good pay, ranging from 4 shillings a day
for the navvies to 10 shillings for the highly skilled, twice what
they could expect to get at home. Expenses were mounting,
and funds in Britain were being hung on to very tightly in the
uncertain times of the Crimean War. But a war which was bad
news for Britain brought good tidings to Canada. As the suppliers of Balkan timber and Ukraine grain were brought to a halt,
so the lumber camps and grain fields of Canada prospered.
And the steadily advancing lines were constantly bringing fresh
opportunities for development. There should, it seemed, have
been ample funds in Canada, but local opinion was turning
against the British contractors. At first, it was taken as a matter
of pride that the line was to be built to the exacting standards
of the very best English routes. Americans simply spiked their
rails down to the sleepers; the British held the rails in metal
chains and used wooden wedges for a firm grip. The American
system had a certain spring to it, whereas the British was
altogether more rigid, and hence there was a strong tendency to
cracking in very cold weather. What once looked like quality
now seemed more like extravagance. American engineers used
materials that were available locally, and were providing ever
grander and more complex timber viaducts. The Canadian line
was passing through forest almost throughout its length, yet
prefabricated iron parts were being sent over from the specially
established Canada Works at Birkenhead on the Mersey.
Rumours flew that Canadian officials had been bribed with share
offers to hand out all this lucrative work to the men from
England. Had they known just what lay ahead, Brassey, Peto
and Company would probably have bribed officials to be released
from their contracts.

At first, the idea had been to rely on local workers, but there
were simply not enough. Brassey came over in person to inspect
the works and suggested that French Canadians should be
recruited from Lower Canada. English and American gangers
were given a guinea a week for each man they signed up and there

103

was soon a good sized workforce. They were not, it soon appeared, an especially useful workforce.

They could ballast, but they could not excavate. They could not even ballast as the English navvy does, continuously working at 'filling' for the whole day. The only way in which they could be worked was by allowing them to fill the wagons, and then ride out with the ballast train to the place where the ballast was tipped, giving them an opportunity of resting. Then the empty wagons went back again to be filled; and so, alternately resting during the work, in that way, they did very much more. They could work fast for ten minutes and they were 'done'. This was not through idleness, but physical weakness. They are small men, and they are a class who are not well fed. They live entirely on vegetable food, and they scarcely ever taste meat.

Even so, they were extra labour, when extra labour was desperately needed. Without their help, many of the experienced navvies could easily have packed up and gone home. Towards the end, mechanical power was brought in to help muscle power. Steam excavators were commonplace in America, but were scarcely used at all in Britain, and the man on the spot in Canada, Mr Rowan, clearly never warmed to the steaming beasts.

Towards the last, in consequence of the extreme cost of labour, we employed steam excavators, not because they were cheaper than men, but because they supplied the want of labour, and enabled us to get on faster. A steam excavator is found to be profitable only in very hard material, such as hard pan, in which a very large force is required to excavate. In lighter materials such as sand or gravel, it is more expensive to use than men at five or six shillings a day.

There was one other factor which the British had failed to take into account, the severity of the Canadian winter. In Ottawa the average temperature between the end of November and the beginning of March is only 16°F (−10°C). Rivers freeze, the ground freezes, snow falls and stays where it drops and outdoor work on railways comes to halt. Costs worked out in the comfort of England looked very uncertain in the ice-locked forests of Canada.

There were difficulties all along the line, but by far the greatest task was the construction of the bridge across the St Lawrence at Montreal. The consulting engineer for the project was Robert Stephenson who had built two bridges in Wales to his own revolutionary design, the first at Conwy, then one across the Menai Straits between the Welsh mainland and Anglesey. Strength and rigidity was provided by the tubes themselves, in effect very long iron boxes; the novel feature was that whereas with most bridges the trains run over the girders, here they ran inside them. Piers were prepared, the two tubes were assembled on site from prefabricated sections, then when all was ready they were floated into position and jacked up. Both the Welsh bridges were a triumphant success. There was, however, a difference in scale. The Menai bridge, the larger of the two, was 1800 feet long; the St Lawrence Bridge, later to be named the Victoria Bridge, was to be 6512 feet long. The St Lawrence itself offered one advantage: the river was shallow and ran over a bed of rock, so there were good foundations for building the piers. Balanced against that was the great winter freeze, and when the thaw set in the builders had to contend with a swift current running in summer at around 8 knots. But engineering difficulties counted for little when set against the human difficulties met by the men who came to build it. The whole story was told in detail by James Hodges who was present throughout the construction period.

The idea for the bridge had first been suggested by a Canadian, John Young, who approached Alexander McKenzie Ross who had been involved in the building of the Conwy bridge. Ross prepared plans which he then took to England to show to Stephenson in the spring of 1852. That autumn Stephenson visited the site himself, approved what he saw and made arrangements for Ross to be appointed as resident engineer. Stephenson himself returned to England to prepare the detailed

105

plans. The tube was to be built in twenty-five sections which were to rest on twenty-four stone piers, and the bridge was to stand 60 feet above the high summer water level at the two spans crossing the navigable channel. The approach at either end was to be along stone-faced embankments. The Victorians were great lovers of accumulated statistics, and on this occasion the figures really do give a notion of the magnitude of the operation:

Total length of the tubes, 6,512 feet

Weight of iron in the tubes, 9,044 tons

Number of rivets in the tubes, 1,540,000

Number of spans, 25; viz. 24 from 242 to 247 feet each, one 330 feet

Quantity of masonry in piers and abutments, 2,713,095 cubic feet

Quantity of timber in temporary works, 2,280,000 cubic feet

The force employed in construction included 6 steam boats and 75 barges, representing together 12,000 tons, and 450 horse power

3,040 men

144 horses

4 locomotive engines

The iron work was prepared at Birkenhead and drilled ready for assembly under the supervision of Robert's cousin, George Robert Stephenson. To pile on a few more statistics: the centre tube consisted of 10,309 separate pieces, drilled with half a million holes and each piece fitted perfectly and every hole was in place. Human and natural elements were not so easily controlled.

The forces which any bridge across the St Lawrence has to withstand are immense. Ice begins to appear in December in places where the flow is gentle. Then as winter cold deepens the ice begins to accumulate in great masses several feet thick which at any moment, perhaps caused by a temporary thaw, may be released from their resting place to thunder down the stream. Gradually the ice packs together to form a solid immovable mass that spreads from bank to bank and there it stays until the thaw. Then, once again, it breaks up and the floes continue their crashing journey downstream until the thaw is complete. The piers of the bridge had to be designed to take the pressure of the tubes, the equally strong pressure of winter ice and the impact of the careering floes. They were given substantial masonry centres to withstand the pressure and needed well-shaped cutwaters to deflect the ice-packs. A very obvious first requirement was a source of good stone. The best stone turned out to be in Indian land, so a meeting with the Indian occupants was arranged for a Sunday afternoon. Thirteen chiefs arrived, in full regalia of paint and feathered head-dresses, but the British engineers found them to be a rather sorry sight – old, care-worn and dirty. Colonial expansion had not been kind to the country's original inhabitants. The Indians in their turn were equally unimpressed by Hodges, the principal negotiator, who they considered to be far too young to be taken seriously – he was in fact over forty years old. Agreement, however, was reached and quarries opened at Point Saint Claire, 16 miles west of Montreal but only half a mile from the line of the railway. Work could begin.

On 24 May 1854 the first temporary dam was begun. Caissons, 188 feet long and 90 feet wide were towed out into the channel and sunk, they had to be pumped out, refloated and towed away again each winter to prevent the ice from wrecking them. It was not, however, to be the practical difficulties of the work that made for slow progress. Disease haunted the workings. In winter, the men who had come over from England and were wholly unprepared for the conditions, suffered dreadfully. Many suffered from frostbite of noses, ears and feet. The fine snow blowing into their faces combined with the brilliance of the sun caused temporary blindness. Summer offered no respite. Along with the warm weather came 'ship fever' or cholera and at one time as many as one in three were laid low. A great many never recovered. Hodges recorded his dismay at the number of strikes: 'Besides strikes occasioned by other causes, it is almost a custom in Canada for mechanics and labourers to strike twice a year, let the rate of wages be what it may. The first period of general strike is in the Spring when increased activity in every business is occasioned by the arrival of the Spring fleet. The second is at commencement of harvest, where there is abundant demand for labour.'

Hodges also faced technical problems. Before leaving England he had left plans for a 'steam traveller' which was to be used for shifting stone at the site. A machine was duly built, shipped to Canada and found to be totally useless. The expensive machine was abandoned and one of the sub-contractors, Mr Chaffey, built a new one in the winter of 1854–5. It had none of the finished elegance of the English machine, but it had one distinct advantage – it worked. It was, in effect, a travelling crane running along rails on a 50-foot-high gantry, and it made the moving and sorting of the huge blocks of limestone a comparatively simple matter.

The principal difficulty, however, was cash. The Crimean War had sent prices rocketing and made nonsense of estimates. However, the contractors pushed on as fast as they could and in 1859 the bridge was open. Hodges now praised the engineer, contractors and their workforce: 'They have left behind them in Canada an imperishable monument of British skill, pluck, science, and perseverance in this bridge, which they not only designed, but constructed.' They also left behind a fortune spent in construction and the contractors took home a considerable loss rather than the expected profit. There was a general feeling that this was not a sensible way to build railways in Canada. Old world technology did not necessarily have the right answers to New World problems. The problems of the steam traveller were symptomatic of what the Canadians saw as a more general malaise. Why order machines, ironwork or, indeed, skilled men from abroad when all were available more conveniently and at lower price closer to home? Increasingly they looked to American experience as a more reliable guide to Canadian development than that offered by the very different railway world of Britain. And British engineers found that as they travelled the world as peripatetic railway builders they too met circumstances where America offered a more useful model. Laying out a line among the green fields of Kent was not at all the same as setting out a route through dense uncharted forests. James Robert Mosse wrote a short treatise on *The Principles to be Observed in the Laying Out of Railways in Newly Developed Countries*. In densely forested areas there was, in his opinion, 'no better method than that practised in America'.

The party generally consists of four surveyors with from twelve to twenty men as chain-men, axe-men, carriers of baggage, &c.; they are furnished with tents and provisions, and where practicable with two or more horse-teams. The surveyors include the chief of the party, the theodolite man, the leveller, one man taking cross-sections, and one spare surveyor.

After obtaining what knowledge of the country is practicable from its general features and from the course of rivers, the chief reconnoitres with an aneroid and a compass some 2 or 3 miles in advance of the party, and he then directs the courses to be taken with the trial lines. The theodolite man then cuts these courses in straight lines (not trusting to the compass) puts in pegs every 100 feet, enters in his note-book the courses, width of rivers and streams, and sketches the general topography of the country. The third surveyor records the levels, and the fourth man follows the level, taking at every 100 feet length cross-sections with a clinometer graduated to percentages of inclination, so that if the index mark 6, and the distance be 400 feet, the difference of level between the two points would be 24 feet; and a figured sketch of each cross-section is then entered in the note-book. By this system, the line cut through the forest is levelled and cross-sectioned on the same day; in fact, the ground covered by the cross-sections is thoroughly ascertained. Where the forest is not too thick, an average of 1¼ mile of line can be thus surveyed in one day, provided the axe-men and chain-men are experienced.

The engineering world of the nineteenth century was being turned on its head. The British engineer was no longer teaching the newcomer overseas, he was learning from him. And when it came to railway construction in South America, British and US engineers and contractors were to find themselves in direct competition. And, at times, they found themselves faced with conditions for which even Mr Mosse's carefully formulated rules proved quite inadequate. Yet a visitor to South America could be forgiven for believing that all the local influences were British. Visit the Central Station at Montevideo and the stony faces that frown down on you are those of James Watt and George Stephenson. The station at São Paulo in Brazil is based – loosely it has to be said – on the Houses of Parliament at Westminster. And nowhere is British influence more obvious than in Argentina. The vast curved roof of the Retiro Station at Buenos Aires is held up by ironwork supplied from Liverpool, while the tiles that decorate the booking hall at the Central Station come from Royal Doulton. Out in the country, in the great wild plains of the pampas are little half-timbered stations that seem to have strayed from Surrey. The first railway to be built in South America, admittedly a very minor affair, was in British Guinea and opened in 1848. Impressions are misleading, however: it is, in reality, a more complicated story in which money provides the main theme.

The first thoughts about railway building in the South American continent had a marvellous breadth of vision; nothing was excluded. In 1827 an Englishman resident in Brazil, Charles Grace, sent a petition to the Emperor for permission to build an 'Iron Rail Way' from Rio to Itaqui on the Argentine frontier. He was promised that his proposal would be given careful consideration. Documents accumulated steadily over the next ten years, each carefully filed and docketed, but nothing actually happened and eventually the project died, smothered under a blanket of paper. Then in 1836, the Government of São Paulo granted a splendidly all-embracing concession for 'ways of iron or others of the most modern and perfect invention, or canals, or one thing or another'. Vehicles to use this nebulous transport system could

110

be powered by steam, and if that was unacceptable they could be steamless. It would have required a deal of ingenuity to devise a system that did not fit the bill. There was even provision for a system to be worked entirely by stationary engines to cross the range of coastal mountains. At least engineers were encouraged to come and see for themselves, and shortly after the granting of the concession the British engineer Alfred de Mornay arrived to carry out the first railway survey in the country. Others soon followed and a range of proposals was put forward including one for a system powered by 'elastic water vapour'. Real progress looked likely when an English merchant based in the port of Santos, Fred Forum, proposed a line from there to São Paulo. Matters advanced far enough for a consultation with Robert Stephenson after a cursory survey had been made. The proposed route was undeniably direct, but achieved this by charging headlong at the hills bordering the coast. Stephenson proposed a longer and gentler route along a river valley.

What is of the greatest importance, it is entirely free from works of magnitude, such as render an accurate calculation of expense not only extremely difficult, but absolutely impracticable, for throughout my experience I have found that the application of ordinary estimates to works of extraordinary magnitude is worse than useless, as it never fails to mislead. This remark is peculiarly applicable to your project, for you are preparing to execute work in a country where the facilities are not only few but limited, where the simplest and cheapest, rather than the most refined and expeditious, methods of operation must be made available.

The advice scarcely mattered since neither line was followed. Shortly afterwards in 1845 another British merchant, Thomas Cochrane, was given a concession for a track to São Paulo. All he had to do was raise the money, and he proved himself nothing if not enthusiastic in this regard. He decided he needed a gimmick to pull in possible investors, so he toured the country with a circus using a clown to hand out prospectuses. Whether the Brazilians felt that a railway promoted by a clown lacked gravitas or whether they thought that any railway promoted in Brazil was a bit of a joke is uncertain. In either case, no funds materialized. Eventually legislation was needed to create a climate in which work could actually get under way. The government agreed to make land freely available, and not just enough land to provide space for the tracks. There were land grants along the route, designed to encourage development, and a strip 30 kilometres wide was declared a no-go zone as far as other railway promoters were concerned, ensuring that the pioneers would not be challenged by rivals. New schemes began to appear.

The main problem all the early would-be railway builders came up against was the line of hills running parallel to the coast and rising to a height of nearly 3000 feet, the Serra do Mar. Even road builders found them a major obstacle. Communication between ports on the coastal plain was comparatively simple, but routes inland were another matter. Mule tracks were the main form of transport and long lines of the beasts, each carrying loads of around 250 lbs, would toil up the steep slopes. That was when they were passable at all. In the torrential tropical storms of the region, exposed surfaces were open to the erosion of the rain: rocks were washed away and deep gulleys were carved into the hillside down which the water thundered. When a small town, Petropolis, was established at the top of the Serra as a summer retreat for the court and high officials, a decent road was created to reach it. An idea of the likely cost of rail building can be gauged from the fact that this roadway was costed, by the government, at £40,000 per mile, even when the land came free.

There was, however, a case for a line that would ease the journey along the sandy, dusty plain at the foot of the Serra. A concession was granted to Senor Ireneo Evangelista De Sorze (later Baron Mava) to build the line. William Bragge was brought over from Britain in 1851 and he opted for the 5 ft. 6 in. gauge then in use in Spain. In 1852 before the line was complete Bragge was replaced by another British engineer, Edward Webb, whose first task was to look at ways of extending the line north from Petropolis; the awkward problem of what to do about the towering cliffs of the Serra do Mar was simply put to one side. It was difficult enough surveying on the top of the plateau, as Webb explains. His first problem came with local maps.

Maps there were in name, but they were worse than useless, because some reliance continued to be placed upon them, until their inaccuracy was proved. These maps are little better than itineraries depicted in lines; the distances upon them having been mainly determined, by the daily, or hourly progress of a saddle mule. A mule's march per day, is reckoned at about a Brazilian league, or four miles per hour; and the distance between two places is marked by leagues, regulated by hours. If the roads were rectilinear and horizontal, such a calculation might approach to the truth; but as they bend in all directions, and at times, ascend gradients of 1 in 4, no true distance can be thus laid down on paper. On the same map, for example, an inch will represent at one part, a league, and at an another, two leagues, or more; positions of towns will be found interchanged, and rivers running in impossible directions. The Author was, therefore, obliged to discard these maps. All they are serviceable for is to point out a tolerably true line of coast, and to give the names of interior towns, rivers, mountains, &c., in the various provinces.

Then came the physical ardours of the survey itself.

Gangs of blacks were constantly employed in cutting paths, or headings, through the forests for the chain, theodolite, and level. It often happens, that to bring down one tree, six, or eight others must be felled, so closely do they grow together, and so firmly are their branches united, by ropes of wood. The surveying party lived in tents, and on no occasion desisted from work on account of the tropical rains, or heat. The survey and levels for the selection of a length of main line extending to thirty miles, were executed in four months and a half.

113

At the end of it all, the effort was wasted: the line was not built so Webb went on to finish the Manao Railway instead. This line offered few topographical difficulties other than one 'deep, unhealthy swamp'; the difficulties that did appear were those caused by the lack of even the most basic equipment. Local Indians were disinclined to take up the work, and earned the scorn of the upright English engineer: 'he plants a few banana trees, clears a small patch of ground for the mandioca root, or for the cultivation of black beans and rice, and all he cares for beyond, is to earn a trifle for clothes, rum, and tobacco.' It was, needless to say, well beneath the dignity of any white man to work as a labourer, so the railway was built by slaves. The slave owners on the plantations were paid 1s 4d a day for the use of 'their' men and women; the slaves themselves received approximately 7d a day's worth of food. Webb's only complaint about this system appears to be the high price.

Excavation along the line was carried out by the men, jerking the earth behind their backs with hoes, after which it was collected in baskets by women who carried it away on their heads. In dry weather it was more like dust than soil, and almost useless for building embankments; wet weather was so wet that virtually no work at all was done. Bridges were lightweight timber affairs, put together in a hurry to get the line open. Timber seems an obvious material to use in a country covered in dense forest, but it was that very density that caused the problems. Webb explains:

The Brazilian forests never present considerable areas covered with the same description of good timber, as in the pine forests; a serviceable tree generally stands in the midst of a group of various kinds of no actual value. The labour of dragging the squared balk from the place of its growth is almost inconceivable. A separate path for each piece of timber has, probably, to be cut, and the log has afterwards to be dragged, by bullocks, down precipices, over ravines, and through swamps.

Working conditions were far from ideal.

The district through which the line runs is very swampy, and it proved most unhealthy. All who were engaged in the works, sooner or later, were struck down by marsh fever. The heat, at times, was excessive; the temperature of the ballast, pure quartz, larger than sand and smaller than ordinary gravel, rose to upwards of 140°. Yet sickness in such situations seems attributable, as much to the impurity of the water consumed by the labourers, as to the excessive heat, or to the vitiated air. A supply of pure water to workmen, in similar positions, would repay a large expenditure for its carriage.

The cost of the 11-mile line, counting rolling stock, was about £15,500 per mile. In 1852 a 2-2-2 locomotive by Fairbairn of Manchester took Brazil into the railway age. The first part of the Manua Railway was complete.

There was no great rush into construction following the opening of the Manua Railway, but Baron Manua himself was now a dedicated enthusiast. He revived the idea of the São Paulo Railway and persuaded other Brazilians to join him in the enterprise. They offered a concession with a guaranteed return of 7 per cent on the £2 million capital and a promise that the line could be extended. It was in many ways an attractive proposition, in spite of the physical difficulties, for the line did serve a genuine commercial need: it linked the rich, coffee-growing area of the plateau to the coastal port. Once again, the obvious place to go to raise both finance and find expertise was Britain. Baron Manua had asked local engineers to survey the route, but they had only travelled as far as the edge of the plateau and had abandoned the whole idea. Now a new approach was made to the eminent British engineer James Brunlees who accepted the challenge. Like other leading engineers of the day, he could take on the consultancy without having to leave home, but he needed a trustworthy engineer to go out to Brazil for the survey. His choice was 26-year-old Daniel Fox who had some experience of the mountains having worked on a narrow gauge line in North Wales and done some surveying in the Pyrenees. He also spoke Spanish, which was considered a great advantage in Brazil – where the language is Portuguese! He accepted the job. It turned out to be even more arduous then Webb's surveying work on the Manua.

Only those engineers who have made surveys through tropical forests can form a definite idea of the immense labour involved in the exploration and selection of a railway route in a country like Brazil, and especially on the precipitous and rugged sea face of the Serra do Mar. To add to the difficulties, the whole escarpment, from the deepest gorge to the loftiest peak, is covered with almost impenetrable primeval forests, through which the explorer has to drive narrow paths resembling 'headings'. The exploring party usually remained in the jungle three weeks at a time, living in huts covered with the leaves of the palmetto, exposed to tropical rains and hardships of which it is difficult to convey an adequate idea, and emerging from the woods blanched from want of sunlight, which rarely penetrates the thick gloom of a Brazilian forest.

The greatest difficulty Fox faced was his inability to get a clear sighting of the whole escarpment. At the foot of the cliffs the trees obliterated much of the view and clambering up only showed a narrow portion. On one day he spotted what appeared to be a likely ravine, but at the end they were greeted by a glorious sight but no route for a railway. A high waterfall tumbled down a sheer face, and the energetic young engineer decided to scramble up the side for a closer look. His efforts were rewarded: he spotted the valley of the Rio Mugy, rising at a comparatively gentle angle up through the Serra. He had found his line, but his problems were only starting.

After fifteen months of surveying, Fox was convinced there was no alternative route up the escarpment, but he was still faced with a drop of over 2500 feet in just five miles, an impossible gradient for conventional traction of 1 in 10. Fox's solution was a series of cable-worked inclines. There were four altogether, varying in length from 5842 to 7017 feet but these were by no means the only problems encountered along the way. From São Paulo, the line was continued inland to Jundiahy, 68 miles from the top of the inclines. Work here was no easier than it had been in the climb up the Serra. The land was sliced through with ravines, making necessary a long procession of banks, cuttings, viaducts and tunnels. The loose rock of the mountains revealed an unhappy tendency to slide back into the cuttings. The only solution available to cope with one land slip was to wash it away. A 'considerable mountain stream' was diverted into the cutting and a small army set to work, one part of which was kept busy shovelling the loose material carried down by the water, while the rest used the same spoil to build up flood banks. Gorges were spanned by lattice girder bridges, cuttings were in places almost a hundred feet deep, yet the contractors, Robert Sharpe & Sons, finished within budget and ahead of schedule. The São Paulo Railway remained as a British company well into the twentieth century.

There was a general belief in South America, in the early days, that British involvement in a railway scheme was a sure-fire guarantee of success. Alas, this was not so. Farmers promoted the Dom Pedro – later the Central – Railway. They paid for the Warring Brothers to come from England to survey a route, but had enough good bucolic common-sense to turn down a system that included conquering the Serra using compressed air. In 1854, the Brazilian Embassy in London was authorized to find a contractor to build this problematic line, and they came up with the name of Edward Price. The brief was splendidly vague: it specified merely the gauge (5 ft. 3 in.) and the two termini. The rest was left to Price.

Their decision turned out to be a disaster. The contractor had no affection for expensive earthworks so the line swayed all over the countryside as if it had been laid down by an incorrigible drunk. The workmanship was atrocious. Station buildings were thrown together using the cheapest lath and plaster. Floors were of beaten earth, and not even well-beaten earth – one station waiting room had to be weeded every week to prevent it becoming totally overgrown. He added to the costs by bringing bricklayers from England, although there were perfectly competent workmen

117

available in Brazil. His outstanding achievement was to set a line across a flood plain which disappeared under water every time there was heavy rainfall.

Happily not all lines undertaken by British engineers suffered the same low standards. The Bahia and San Francisco Railway was engineered by Vignoles, with his son Hutton Vignoles as resident engineer. It was a line on which the British had a controlling interest but the workforce was international: 446 Italians, 107 English, 11 Germans, 4 French, 2 Swiss and 2069 Brazilians. The international appeal of Brazil is not difficult to understand: the Brazilians had an enviable reputation for prompt payment of bills and honouring of commitments. When the government spoke of 'guaranteed payments', then they stuck to their word. Webb gave his views of the cosmopolitan workforce in typically blunt terms. The Chinese navvies, who began to appear in 1855, 'were evidently the scum of the population; utterly useless as labourers, they proved a continual source of annoyance and loss, and not one in ten was worth his food.' The Portuguese labourers, on the other hand, were first rate, if a little conservative: they arrived already organized into gangs headed by sub-contractors.

> Each of these men brought with him from sixteen to sixty of his countrymen, and the gangs, thus formed, dotted the line of the works with their triangular huts roofed with grass.
> The Portuguese labourers are a very hardy race of men, who can endure greater privation and exposure than English labourers. At first, they refused to use the barrow and the shovel; the hoe, their only tool, was not, however, so objectionable along the steep sides of the Mangaratiba mountains, as it was on the plains of Manua; and in certain localities, from its acting as pick and shovel combined, it was even the best tool that could have been used.

The railways first executed in Brazil all had this international element as did those in other parts of South America as far as construction was concerned, but the British continued to own lines such as the Central, right through into the twentieth century.

118

Cash spoke louder than the rival claims of local interest, multinational labour forces or old imperial allegiances. Lines throughout South America had an equally strong English accent.

While Brazil was establishing its rail network in the 1850s, neighbouring Argentina scarcely existed as a modern nation-state at all. Large areas were either self governing or scarcely governed at all. There was no rush into railway building largely because no one saw any need for railways: there was no manufacturing industry, no mineral wealth. A few far-sighted individuals did see, however, that railways could play an important political role in pulling the disparate elements of the country together. The group of provinces in the interior, the Argentine Confederation, was a potential nucleus for a unified country, and in 1853, the Confederation spokesman Juan Alberdi spelt it out in the simplest terms: 'railways will bring about the unity of the Argentine Republic better than any number of congresses.' In 1854 the Confederation engaged an American engineer – on the not always sound ground that he was the cheapest available – to survey a line from Cordoba to Rosario. There was then the problem of finding the cash, and the Argentinians approached another American, William Wainwright, to organize the fund-raising. He in turn approached the powerful corpus of British merchants based in Buenos Aires but they had nowhere near enough capital themselves, nor could they raise funds in London where the effects of the Crimean War were being felt. The plans were set aside, but the idea of railways out of Buenos Aires had nonetheless grabbed the imagination of the British merchants.

If grandiose schemes had to be temporarily shelved, a more modest beginning was possible. Daniel Gowland, chairman of the British Merchants committee in Buenos Aires, was one of the most enthusiastic supporters of the Ferrocarril al Oeste, the Western Railway. The local government gave the necessary official support: the building land was free, the capital equipment brought from overseas was exempt from customs duty and they put up a third of the money, but agreed not to take any dividends until private investors were receiving 9 per cent. The arrangements sound as if they were designed to finance an entire rail network, but it was, in fact, no more than a modest suburban line which built up over the years to a less than impressive 25 miles of track. Yet the locals still found it necessary to send to Britain for William Bragge, who came across with 160 navvies in tow. In due time rolling stock and locomotives were sent from England, and to show that the little suburban railway was in reality destined to be part of an altogether vaster enterprise the engines were given stirringly heroic names: *Progreso* and *Luz del Desierto* (Light of the Desert). The line was built to a broad, 5ft. 6in. gauge as were lines already begun in Brazil and Paraguay. This decision was attacked by Argentinian patriots who declared that the gauge had been set not out of any rational drive to link up with neighbouring railways, but because second-hand rolling stock from the Crimea was beginning to come on to the market.

In May 1862 General Bartolome Mitre became President of Argentina, and the previously independent province of Buenos Aires came, if only partly, under the control of the new national government. There now began a period of western-style economic expansion which coincided with the new legislation in Britain that gave joint-stock companies their legal basis. It was a happy conjunction: Argentina wanted money for investment, Britain had the cash looking for a profitable home. And the Argentinian schemes were potentially very profitable indeed, with government guaranteed returns and handsome land grants. The cynical might say that the taxpayers of South America were being forced to hand out expensive sweeteners to the wealthy investors of Britain; defenders of the scheme would ask how else railways were ever to be built. Whatever the morality of the scheme, it certainly attracted funds. By 1875 over £23 million had been invested in Argentina of which nearly a third went on railway construction.

The impetus for railway building came, as it had in Brazil, very largely from the British merchants who had set up in business there. The leading figure was G.W. Drabble who had first come to Buenos Aires in 1842 as representative of the family's cotton-exporting firm based in Manchester. He stayed on and eventually became Chairman of the Bank of London and River Plate and

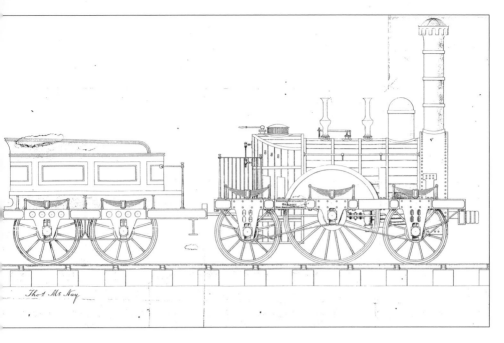

1. Timothy Hackworth's locomotive, built for the first Russian railway in 1836.

2. A double-ended Fairlie locomotive built by the Vulcan Foundry in 1872. It became Locomotive No.2 on the Dunedin & Port Chalmers Railway, New Zealand.

3. The articulated Beyer Garratt locomotive – in effect, a conventional locomotive, with a second power unit at the front – seen here on the Benguela Railway in Africa in the 1920s.

4. A 2-6-0 standard gauge locomotive being loaded at the Armstrong-Whitworth Scotswood works in 1928 for the Egyptian State Railway.

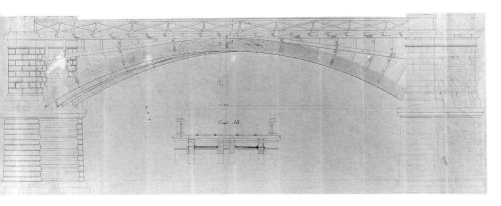

. A drawing from William Mackenzie's office of an arch of the viaduct across the Seine on the Paris to Rouen Railway (1840s).

6. Construction of the Pojucca tunnel on the Bahia to San Francisco railway, engineered by Vignoles (1860s).

7. A construction train in the San Ramon ravine on the Santiago & Valparaiso Railway, for which William Lloyd was engineer (1860s).

8. A section of the Attach Bridge being raised into place on the Northern Punjab Railway, December 1882.

9. Looking west from the Attach Bridge as the railway heads off towards the mountains, March 1882.

10. One of the famous loops that help the Darjeeling Himalayan Railway climb.

11. The Tientsin Pukow Railway at Hsu Chou Fu (China); the British engineer's bungalow can be seen in the background (1890s).

12. Lions Rock before it was blasted away to make room for the Kandy to Colombo Railway, Sri Lanka (1860s).

13. The elegant ironwork – made in Britain – at Colombo Station, Sri Lanka.

14. Surveyors A.E.Pike and D.E.Mercer surveying in dense bush in Eastern Nigeria (1900s).

15. Sub-contractors pose at an engineer's camp in the Gold Coast in Eastern Nigeria.

16. Building the approach to Carter Bridge for Nigerian Railways in 1900.

17. Indian platelaying gangs moving camp on the Uganda Railway (1900s).

18. Moving trucks along an incline in the Great Rift Valley on the Uganda Railway (1900s).

19. A reverse on the Mau Escarpment on the Uganda Railway (1900s).

20. Ferrying the first locomotive to reach British Central Africa across the Oyan River in 1900.

21. The Great Lithgow zigzag in New South Wales, Australia (1870s).

22. Launching a caisson out into the river during the construction of the
Albert Bridge, Australia (1890s).

23. Not suburban England in the nineteenth century, but an outback station in New South Wales.

24. The Fell engine climbing the Rimutaka incline in New Zealand, 1878; the central rail that was gripped by horizontal wheels can clearly be seen.

the principal promoter of the Central Argentine Railway. However assiduously local interests promoted the line, however, there was no disguising the fact that they were a good deal less enthusiastic about paying for it. The largest sum, invested by the richest family in the country, was £200 which contrasts with the £20,000 invested by a Mrs Sanders of whom nothing very much is known except that she lived in Derbyshire. Not surprisingly those most closely involved in construction were the major investors. On the Buenos Ayres Great Southern, the engineer who took the first contract, Thomas Rumball, was a heavy subscriber, as were the contractors, Brassey and Wythes, Peto and Betts. They acted wisely, for the success of the line ensured an excellent return. At the opposite extreme, financially as well as geographically, was the Northern Railway of Buenos Ayres (*sic*). It was promoted in England by E.H.S. Crawford MP and was to run from Buenos Aires to the Rio Maldonado at San Fernando where a new deep-water port was to be constructed. It was from the first a story of muddle and incompetence. When the line was open there seemed to be no shortage of passengers, but receipts were depressingly low. It was only when someone was sent to investigate that it was discovered that local railway employees were taking out sheaths of tickets and selling them from a booth outside the station at a third of the regular price.

Everyone expected to get something out of the railways. The government had fine phrases for each new opening ceremony. When Mitre took the ceremonial spade to inaugurate work on the Central in 1863, he declared that 'Everyone must rejoice on the opening of this road, for it will tend to give riches where there is poverty and to institute order where there is anarchy.' The railway would, the government hoped, encourage settlement along the route as the lines struck out into the open plains of the pampas, hence the land grants. It was a point not lost on speculators. They could buy land on the cheap and as the railway approached, sell on at great profit. The sharper practitioners realized that they did not even have to do that. They could buy up land, announce that they were promoting a railway over it, sell the land – and forget all about the railway. Mitre at least managed to stop this particular scam by announcing that the government would decide where railways were to be built, leaving it to private capital to finance them.

There was something of a confrontation between the British entrepreneurs and the American interests led by William Wheelwright. In 1862 Wheelwright finally got the concession to build the Central, the line he first proposed from Cordoba to Rosario. At the same time, the British group led by Edward Lumb was authorized to build the Great Southern from Buenos Aires to Chascomus. There were tax exemptions, land grants and guaranteed returns for both parties. The British got the more favourable guarantee, at a return of 7 per cent on a capital investment set at £10,000 per mile; Wheelwright, for his part, received a more generous land grant. He decided, however, that cash in hand was a better bargain than land and objected to the terms offered to the British interest. Lumb's group won, not because they necessarily had a better case, but because they were more generous in their dishing out of bribes. It was estimated that they paid £22,000 to various officials. Work on the Great Southern got under way and an interesting array of speculators, engineers and contractors descended on the country. There was no question but that they did well out of it. Where locals used paper money issued by local banks – the bank of Cordoba, for example, circulated 33 million pesetas in notes, while holding 8 million in gold – the railway men got their cash in gold. The government kept handing out reserves, hoping one day it would come back in investment. Eventually the tail did manage to catch up with the dog.

The railway builders had a different view to the speculators: they saw themselves as public benefactors helping a backward country to achieve its rich potential. Helps in his biography of Brassey wrote, 'I think that this Argentine enterprise of Mr Brassey's will have more important results than any other of his undertakings', and again, 'I doubt whether, in the history of railway enterprise, there has been anything so largely beneficial to the country wherein a railway has been introduced.' The contractors were not merely railway builders, that was the easy part. Indeed, the going was so easy for much of the way that all the navvies had to do was lay the sleepers on bare earth and spike the rails to them. These contractors were also colonisers, opening up the country, encouraging immigrants to settle. The railways themselves created a demand as the British Chargé d'Affaires reported in 1866: 'The supply falls very short of the demand, and unlimited employment can be procured without difficulty at most remunerative wages, as in this country artisans and labourers are greatly needed.' Railway workers flooded in, mainly from Spain and Italy, with a few from Britain. They mostly took their wages, finished the job and went home again. Railway empire building did not go quite as planned: the men came as migrant workers, not as settlers. Nevertheless, until Peron took over all the railways in the country, the British had built and still owned some 16,000 miles of track in Argentina. They were never to dominate any other South American country to the same extent; for most of the rest of the region the dominant figure was supplied by the USA in the form of the swashbuckling contractor Henry Meiggs. That does not mean that the British did not make significant contributions to the work elsewhere. In 1865, for example, the Central Uruguay Railway was promoted using a guarantee that began at 7 per cent and when it was increased to 8 per cent on capital set at £10,000 per mile English contractors stepped in; it was the Argentine story all over again. When the line opened, much of the rolling stock and most of the locomotives were from England – specially-built components from Robert Stephenson, engines from such well-known companies as Beyer Peacock, Manning Wardle and Vulcan. More challenging situations appeared further south.

The story of construction in Chile brings back an engineer we last met in Scandinavia, William Lloyd. On his return to England in 1853 he heard that the Chilean government was looking for a railway engineer and Robert Stephenson recommended him for the job. This time he took his wife and two young children with him. It is easy to underestimate the sheer scale of the adventure it was for the railway pioneers and their families, setting off on long and difficult journeys for unknown lands. At least Valparaiso, their destination, was a civilized place. When Charles

Darwin came with the *Beagle* in 1834 he declared it 'a sort of London or Paris' where one was 'obliged to shave & dress decently'. This may have been encouraging for the Lloyd family, but first they had to get there.

The outward journey started pleasantly enough, with a voyage by paddle steamer across the Atlantic to New York. Then their troubles started. The Californian gold rush that had begun in 1849 had not yet run its course, and there was still a huge demand for ships to take the fortune hunters either all the way round Cape Horn to California or at any rate as far as Panama, from where they could take the fetid trail across the isthmus to the west coast. Anything that could float was pressed into service and no niceties, such as limiting the numbers that could be crammed in, were observed. The Lloyds booked passage on a ship, which turned out to have started its life as the Vanderbilt's 200-ton yacht, days of glory which were now faded memories. The Lloyd family found themselves in the company of 900 rough and rowdy gold diggers. They left the overcrowded vessel on Panama's east coast and took to the partly built railway across the isthmus, finally finishing their journey to Panama itself by mule. It was not a welcoming sight: 'a mouldering den of fever grog shops, low gambling halls, of flies, mosquitoes, oppressive heat and social disorganisation.' It was with a good deal of relief that they boarded ship again. Almost the first passenger they met was Lloyd's old navvy companion from French days, Tom Breakwater. He was *en route* for Peru, but already had succumbed to one of the fevers that haunted Central America. Within a day he was dead. The Lloyds were more fortunate and all made the journey of sixty-three days safely.

In the annals of railway building it is easy to overlook the role of wives and families who followed the men to remote parts of the world. No one has written the story of the numerous Mrs Lloyds, uprooted from home, bringing up families among strangers. There was one consolation: Valparaiso had a large English community of merchants and traders who here in the southern hemisphere played cricket and rode to hounds as if they were back in Surrey or Berkshire. William Lloyd, however, had some unpleasant surprises in store.

He had left England under the impression that he was required to 'put the finishing touches' to the railway from Valparaiso to Santiago: he was not to know that no one had yet done very much in the way of starting touches. There was no equipment worth mentioning and no trained workforce.

By him, the Chilian navvy, who had all his life transported earth or other material in hide bags on his back, the wheel of a barrow was regarded as an ornament, not for use, therefore he hoisted the clumsy contrivance on to his shoulder in triumph.

The only way he could get them to use even the simplest cranes was to threaten them with the sack if they refused. Lloyd tackled the problems he met with great vigour. He soon found that though his Indian workforce knew nothing of western techno-logy, they were totally honest and trustworthy and he developed a great respect for them. He had no respect for the site chosen for Valparaiso station when he first rode out to see it. It was in a poor area, where the streets were 'almost girth-deep in foetid mud' and surrounded by a huddle of crude, insanitary fishermen's huts. Lloyd had the huts pulled down and arranged for new, far better houses to be built at the railway company's expense and for the foul swamp that was left behind to be filled in. All this then had to be protected by a sea wall – by no means the last to be built on the line. The first section of line ran out along the foot of the cliffs, and at one place a tunnel had to be cut through a spur of rock. It was the first railway tunnel on the Pacific Coast, so the completion in 1855 was marked by an official breakfast and a rendition by the local band of God Save the Queen. They began track laying in May of that year and they set a target of completing the first eight miles in time for another official opening on 18 September, Independence Day. The track was completed on time, but there was a problem. Two locomo-tives had arrived, crated up, but there were no fitters and no driver. Lloyd showed his customary resourcefulness and inveigled a ship's engineer from a visiting mail steamer to help him set up the engines. Together they drove the first train in triumph.

Work was going well, but ahead lay a formidable obstacle. The line had to pass through the outlying hills of the Campana Mountains in a long tunnel. The contract was given to a local man, in spite of Lloyd's protestations that he had no experience: local pride won the day. Lloyd washed his hands of the affair and got on with constructing the line on the far side of the ridge. The inevitable happened, the contractor folded and eighteen months were spent in legal wrangles. Meanwhile the track was still advancing, and Lloyd once again displayed his ingenuity. He built inclines up either side of the ridge and hauled a locomotive up to the top to act as a stationary engine. There it remained as a 'temporary expedient' for four years, pulling trucks up one side and lowering them down the other. Things began to improve in 1860 when he was finally given control of the tunnel workings. Even then he had his problems. On one occasion a German sub-contractor announced that he had no money to pay his 300 navvies, and he had no intention of standing in front of that many angry men and telling them so. The task went to Lloyd who had to suffer the consequences. He was forced to escape to a wooden house which was pelted with stones and there he stayed until the militia came to rescue him.

Lloyd had done his best, but by 1861 only 33 miles of railway had been completed. The task required greater resources than he had at his disposal. At this stage, Henry Meiggs stepped in and offered to finish the line in three years for 6 million pesos, with a bonus of 510,000 pesos for every month he came in ahead of that term. The deal was struck and within two weeks there were 4000 men at work – the line was completed in two years, three days – with a very handsome bonus. Lloyd had already moved on.

He was to work on other lines in Chile. In 1861 he was put in charge of the 33-mile long Coquimbo Railway. The first section was financed by the government who paid half and a consortium consisting of two Chilean and one English banker who paid the rest. There was a difficult passage through the mountains involving three tunnels, a 150-foot-high viaduct and a steady rise on a cruel gradient of 1 in 44 for twelve miles. There was one extravagant example of 'cut and fill' where spoil from a 70-foot-deep cutting went to build up an astonishing 300-foot-high embankment. At least the task facing the locomotives was not as severe as on a line in the silver-mining district on which he was asked to report and which he discovered had the alarming gradient of 1 in 20.

At the end of his work on the Santiago line, Lloyd stayed for another six months to ensure that everything was in good order and then headed home for England and, he believed, an interlude of peace and quiet. It was not to be. He had scarcely got his feet up in front of the fire before a request came through for him to return to South America to build a line in Mexico. He agreed, but this time the family stayed at home: Mexico in the 1860s, torn by revolution, ravaged by bandits, was not the ideal spot to take his wife and children, particularly as he was offered the job because his English predecessor had been murdered. The line was to run from Vera Cruz to Mexico City, a difficult line made doubly difficult by the presence of two armies, the French army of occupation and the Emperor Maximilian's Austrian troops. Lloyd seemed remarkably sanguine about the whole thing:

> I knew also that a few miles of line had been made and opened for traffic under the direction of an English engineer, who had been shot dead in a train by brigands, and I therefore was by no means unprepared to find that the direction of these works over a hundred leagues in a mountainous and sparsely populated country could entail considerable personal risk to health and life; therefore I took the precaution, of considerably increasing my life insurance, and of adding a medical officer to my staff.

In October 1864 he set sail for Vera Cruz. First impressions were even worse than those he had found in Panama. Vera Cruz was 'a foul and miserable place' with 'a festering reef in front, extensive swamps hard by, high walls all round the city, and no water supply.' Not surprisingly, it was infected with yellow fever. After Vera Cruz even a journey through bandit country made a welcome change. He took a 20-mile journey to Cameron along the line on which his predecessor had been shot, and found that a branch line to the north was totally unusable because of bandits. The next step of the journey, a 30-mile ride to the hills, was by diligence – the stage coach familiar from a thousand Hollywood Westerns. Lloyd was taken ill on the journey so they were forced to make a stop at a French army post, where they found matters were even worse. Fever had laid everyone low, including the army doctor, and Lloyd's own doctor was soon earning his keep. Forty hours later they set off again for the mountain pass with a guard of twelve Mexican lancers who, Lloyd said, looked highly picturesque but inspired little confidence. The coach stuck deep in the mud, but even so they overtook a dispirited band of French soldiers, one of whom was lying motionless, face down on the ground. It rapidly became clear that he was neither sick nor injured but just plain drunk. He reeled to his feet and the first thing he saw was the brightly uniformed lancers. These he decided must be the enemy come to kill him and he began shooting. Had he been a touch more sober he might even have hit someone. To an outside observer it might have been hilarious – the terrified lancers, the roaring drunk, the astonished Englishman – but this incident was probably a lot less amusing for the weak, sick engineer confronted by an inebriated soldier firing real shot from a real gun. They went on through dense forest until they emerged on the high plateau where the highway led on to Mexico City and its background of snow-capped mountains. The dangers and trials were over, if only for a time, and Lloyd and his party settled into a comfortable house that was to be home base.

The first task they faced was surveying, and headquarters was established at the entrance to the pass of Maltrata. This time they were given real protection in the form of a troop of cavalry and a company of infantry. By 1865 work was under way with thousands of South American Indian workers. They arrived with their entire families and looked after their own food and lodgings.

On the line, the women and children filled baskets with earth, which the men then carried away. Each Friday night they all left for home and each Monday morning they were back again. At the height of the working period there were around ten thousand of them and Lloyd declared that 'a score of British workmen would have given him more difficulty to control'. There were problems, however. Each month around £25,000 had to be brought as far as 300 miles through bandit country to pay the workers, and the railway company had no option but to set up their own private army to protect it. Compared with this, building a railway might have seemed easy. In fact the route was far from simple, with a descent from the mountains to 4000 feet at 212 feet per mile. He pushed on until 140 out of the 300-mile route was completed and another hundred miles was ready for track laying. Then politics and a financial crisis brought everything to a halt and Lloyd left Mexico, just in time to miss the revolution that swept away the French. He was probably disappointed, for his undimmed sense of adventure spurred him on to further work in South America.

He surveyed routes in Argentina and Brazil, the latter proving just as exciting as his escapades in Mexico. This time, however, the problems were rather more natural than man-made. He surveyed a vast amount of ground including a section along the River Iraby. It was fearsome country with jungle reaching to the water's edge and no settlements for 260 miles. Previously two corps of engineers had been sent out but had achieved nothing. No food had got through to them; the jungle was too dense for hunting, and they were terrified of the native Indians. Lloyd sorted that out. He had stout canoes built and hacked regular portage tracks round the rapids so that a supply route could be maintained. The engineers welcomed the food supplies, but they would much rather have been told to go home. The river was never safe. A tropical storm turned it into a torrent, and at one time Lloyd had to abandon his hut even though it was built 30 feet above the waterline. Other surveyors had equally strenuous tasks, on the Matto Grosso and up the River Parana, which in places was six miles across. For two years they lived under canvas in a hostile environment, but the task was eventually completed. William Lloyd was only one of a number of engineers working in the Americas in equally appalling conditions – we know his story simply because he lived to a comfortable retirement during which he wrote his memoirs.

Throughout the region there were engineers and contractors at work on lines large and small. In 1915, the Royal Navy built the Camber narrow-gauge railway along the northern edge of Stanley harbour in the Falkland Islands; it ran from Navy Point to the radio transmitters at the edge of Port Stanley, a modest distance of around four miles. It would scarcely be worth a mention were it not for one idiosyncratic feature. The wind in the Falklands is notorious, so the little trucks were built with sockets into which a mast could be fitted. A small lug sail was attached enabling personnel to bowl along the track at some speed. More conventional transport was provided by a pair of Kerr Stuart 'Wren' class locomotives, and the author was delighted to discover that they had survived the 1982 war. They sit on the quayside, rusty, far from complete, but still there, having been hauled off a rubbish dump. Something at least has survived of the very last line to be built by the British in South America.

CHAPTER FIVE

Asia

Early railway building in Asia was inseparably entwined with the process of colonization. Britain had not set out to acquire an Asian empire, but had more or less stumbled into it by the early nineteenth century. At its heart was the vast territory of India. It is not possible to understand the complexities of railway building here without first having at least a notion of the underlying political situation. Even the name 'India' has meant different things to different people at different times; it has never been prudent to anticipate a long shelf-life for a map of India.

The British had very little interest in the Indian sub-continent during the early years of exploration and colonization. When Elizabeth I granted a royal charter bestowing trading rights in Asia, it went to the East India Company. The name is significant: the objective was the spice islands of the East Indies but unfortunately the Dutch had got there first and established territorial rights and a trading monopoly. They were also strong enough to defend their position. The British looked instead to India. That country was already carved up into areas of influence. Much of the land was ruled by the Moghuls who had migrated south from Persia early in the sixteenth century. The early British traders must have been overwhelmed by the capital Agra, with its opulent temples and palaces behind massive fortress walls. And by 1632 they could have looked downriver to where that most famous of all Indian palaces was being built, the Taj Mahal. But already the Moghul Empire was beginning to slide and disintegrate and two

131

European powers, France and Portugal, had important enclaves. There was plenty of room still for the British to shoulder their way in and join in the wholesale exploitation of the country. International rivalries were inevitable: the native princes quarrelled with each other, and France and Britain were soon at war. The Seven Years War began in Europe but spread to India, and the British victory signalled an end to French involvement in the sub-continent. The Portuguese were more concerned with religious introspection than trade, and they were left to their tiny enclave of Goa. By the end of the eighteenth century, the most effective force in India was neither the government nor the princes, but the privately run trading empire of the East India Company. In 1765 Robert Clive, commander of the British forces, formally accepted the state revenue of Bengal, making that state, in effect, a colony – and one that was to be stripped of its assets with no thought for the future. The age of the nabobs had arrived, the men who went out to India, nominally to serve Britain, in practice to serve themselves and come home flaunting huge wealth. It was all very well being flamboyant in India, but in Britain it caused deep resentment and envy. The government acted. There was now to be a division between trade and administration, and the two should never again mingle. No administrator could ever again legally use his public office for private profit. It was a difficult and confused time: India, or a large part of it, was effectively under British rule, but relations with the British Parliament were distant. The Governor General could – and did – overrule his Council. There was an excellent Civil Service – the best paid anywhere in the world – and two armies, one owing allegiance to the Crown, the other to the East India Company. It all made for complexity, and complexity does not make for decisive rapid action, as the early railway promoters were to discover.

The case for railways was easily made. Trade with Britain meant that communication and transport had taken on a new importance; and the current state of the roads was atrocious. It is always difficult to assess accounts of bad transport systems of a century and a half ago, but in the case of India one can at least

use the yardstick of the modern road system. Most would come
to the conclusion that if this is what the roads are like at the end
of the twentieth century, they must have been truly appalling 200
years ago. Even today, traffic is dominated by the lumbering cart
drawn by bullock or camel or by pack animals. An engineer
visiting India while the railways were first being planned wrote,

> Indian railways will not, therefore, as in England, be the
> substitution of a perfect system of conveyance for other
> convenient means, at the demand of a prosperous nation;
> but they will be, at least in many districts, the first introduc-
> tion of any communication whatever.

A civil servant described a twelve-hour journey which involved
seven hours of bone-rattling travel over a dirt track masquerading
as a main road: 'On his way the *manslutdar* amused us with
several stories of accidents which had occurred on this road, one
of which related to the sad fate of a *banion*, or trader, who
received such a jolt as to make him inadvertently bite the end of
his tongue off.' There were, however, more pressing needs for
transport improvement than to improve the travel conditions for
junior civil servants. India was attempting to build up a prosperous cotton exporting industry. Mr Mangle, one time Chairman
of the East India Company, had no doubts about what was
holding back the process: 'I have made the largest admissions with
reference to the want of roads, which I say, is the only real
obstacle to the exportation of cotton in large quantities from
India.' Other powerful interests found the lack of efficient transport a severe hindrance. Sir William Andrews put the military
point of view and quoted a telling example:

> In 1845, when the First Sikh War broke out, all officers,
> whose regiments were in the field, were ordered to join the
> army. About 100 engineer, cavalry and infantry officers
> were required to go from Calcutta to the north-west frontier
> of India. They were sent at the public expense, and with the
> greatest despatch, but the Postmaster-General could only

send three daily! As the journey took 16 days, travelling day and night, few of these officers rejoined their regiments before the war was over.

This could, of course, be taken as an argument that armies manage perfectly well without their officers, but it also reinforces the point that no one in British India was happy with the old transport system inherited from the Moghuls. The army were to become builders of railways on their own account, though some of the officers seem to have been afflicted by decidedly wild notions. One military engineer, Lieutenant Colonel John Kennedy, began his proposals for construction with a full-scale tirade in which he 'condemned heartily and completely, all that railway engineers had accomplished in England.' One of his fellow officers, Lieutenant Colonel L.W. Grant, was so worried about the threat from wild animals, that he proposed hanging an entire railway from chains; the resulting track was eight feet above the ground, like a vastly elongated suspension bridge. Happily, other military engineers had rather more practical, and conventional, schemes to put forward.

The main impetus for railway construction, however, came from the civil section of Indian life – indeed the beginnings can be put down largely to one enthusiastic individual, Rowland Macdonald Stephenson. His ambitions, according to a piece in the *Calcutta Review* in 1856, were large. He wanted 'to girdle the world with an iron chain, to connect Europe and Asia from the furthest extremities by one colossal Railway . . . to connect so much of the two continents as should enable a locomotive to travel from Calcutta to London with but two breaks, one at the Straits [Dover] and one at the Dardanelles.' His early proposals had a more limited end: to see a line built that would join Calcutta, then the capital, to Delhi. Stephenson had the advantage of a sound background in civil engineering and a long family connection with India. An ancestor had negotiated a treaty on behalf of the East India Company, and other members of the family had kept up the tradition. Only his father had let the side down, absconding from the firm in which he was a partner and taking the company cash box with him. Perhaps Stephenson's enthusiasm for public works stemmed from a desire to restore the family honour. He himself worked for a while for the East Indian Steam Navigation Company which lost out to the Peninsular and Oriental (P&O). When in 1841 he began his propaganda war, his background and experience ensured that he was given a hearing, but it was not until 1844 that he gained a positive response. He wrote to the government of Bengal and received an encouraging reply: he had found a supporter in the important figure of the Deputy Governor. The Secretary to the government wrote, 'The Deputy Governor desires me to add that he is deeply sensible of the advantages to be gained by construction of Rail Roads along the principal lines of communication throughout the country, and is anxious to afford to any well-considered project for that purpose his utmost support.' And to make clear that this was not a casually issued offer of help, the Deputy Governor published his reply in the *Calcutta Gazette*.

Armed with the goodwill of the government and with the backing of local merchants, Stephenson set off to promote his line, now christened the East India Railway, in the money markets of London. British investors had never shown themselves particularly keen to put their cash into schemes in distant India and they were no more enthusiastic about railways. They would only invest if the government put up cash as well. This was not very encouraging, and Stephenson went on to approach the Court, the ruling body of the East India Company, with a good deal more trepidation than he had shown when contacting the government of Bengal. He suggested that they should offer to guarantee a comparatively modest return of 4 per cent on capital, but even this was more than the Company was prepared to offer. They came up with an array of reasons why the railways would not work: the country was poor, no one could afford to travel, and there would not be enough freight traffic to make good the difference. Could they get competent engineers? Would beetles attack the wooden sleepers? Would track be washed away in the monsoon? The list of obstacles seemed so long that it must have come as a pleasant surprise to Stephenson that the East India

Company ended up offering anything at all. In the end, however, it offered to pay for a survey.

In 1845 F.W. Simms set out for India to begin the work. He turned out to be just the man the Company did not want for the job: instead of confirming their wholly negative views, he proved an enthusiast capable of out-enthusing Stephenson himself. After covering the ground with two military engineers as companions, he declared that there was no reason at all why railways could not be built in India and furthermore young Indians could be trained to run them. He wholly approved Stephenson's 900-mile proposed route and put up a case for the whole line being built and operated by a single company. The Under Secretary for the government was only one of many in India who had doubts about funding.

Is it possible that England will send to India the enormous sums which may be required? Other countries have effected works of great magnitude out of their own wealth, but India must look to England for the necessary capital. She must ask back a portion of the tribute which for years past she has paid to England.

This pessimism was not unwarranted. Company and government could not agree on how railways were to be built, where they were to be built or how they were to be paid for. Meanwhile other schemes were coming forward.

In 1844, the Bombay Great Eastern Railway was formed with the intention of building a $53\frac{1}{2}$-mile route from Bombay to the Western Ghats, the line of cliffs over 300 miles long that rises up over a thousand feet from the coastal plain of western India – presenting just the sort of barrier that had faced the engineers working in South America. It looked on paper to be a thoroughly sound venture backed by an array of worthies, ranging from Sir Bartle Frere, Private Secretary to the Governor, to minor government officials, British traders and merchants, and leaders of the Indian mercantile community. The promoters had taken advice from a friend of Frere's, the engineer George T. Clark who

136

had come to India in 1842. The government committee set up to study the prospectus was not, however, greatly impressed. The costs were, they declared, pure guesswork since there had been no survey and the route had not been studied 'by any party whose evidence, written or verbal, we had the opportunity of obtaining'. If the scrutinisers were dubious about the costs, that was as nothing compared with the scorn with which they treated the estimates of revenue. The promoters had boldly prophesied a return of 22½ per cent; the committee came up with a figure of one eighth of one per cent – though they conceded that with an improved plan, a modest 4¾ per cent might just be attainable. This was all very discouraging, but now a new contender appeared on the field with an even more ambitious scheme. John Chapman was an engineer recently arrived from England, but he identified a genuine need that only a railway could meet. His Great Indian Railway would unite the cotton fields of the interior with the Port of Bombay. His idea could hardly have come at a better time. In 1846 the cotton crop of America failed and the mills of Lancashire were starved of raw material. They looked to India to fill the gap.

So it was that in the mid-1840s, two railway systems were being promoted, each of which promised tangible advantages to British interests. In the east, a railway could bring coal to the port of Calcutta, a vast advantage to the burgeoning steamship lines. In the west, the other route would feed the seemingly insatiable demands of the cotton mills. Real progress seemed possible, but still the East India Company dithered and wavered. However clear the matters might seem to engineers like Simms who had surveyed the land or to the merchants on the spot who understood the needs of local markets, the men in London who had ultimate control were not convinced. But there was leverage that could be applied. The East India Company charter was shortly coming up for renewal, and although the British government was not directly involved in the railway question, it was very much in control of that charter. Impassioned pleas came out of India. An anonymous pamphlet addressed to Lord John Russell was a patchwork of purple prose:

England, the Lilliputian island, rich and selfish as a pampered glutton, has indulged to excess in the luxury of Railways. Let her now resign herself to repose and the needful process of digestion, while her slave, the giant continent of India, feeble from inanition and sick at heart from hope deferred, is permitted to break her fast upon the superfluity of her master's abundance.

The East India Company gave way under the pressure, and agreed first to a 3 per cent and then – when that was shown to be too meagre to attract much in the way of funds – a more generous 5 per cent guarantee. The East Indian Railway Company and the Great Indian Peninsula Railway were given the green light – or perhaps more accurately the amber. Each was authorized to build a comparatively short length of track: from Calcutta to Raneegunge, 120 miles of the originally planned 900 miles in the former case; and Bombay to Kalyan, just 30 miles, in the latter. The agreements contained some clauses which were incredibly generous to the infant railway companies. If the railways made a loss, the East India Company would take them over and repay all the money that had been spent. Having ceded so much, the East India Company tried to protect their investment by exercising control over just about everything. The arrangements read like a recipe for chaos. There were to be two engineers in charge, one appointed by the railway company, one by the government. The railway engineer would create a design or a plan which was then passed to the consulting engineer for approval. If the latter agreed, all well and good. If not the matter was referred to the Indian government, and any arguments there were sent to the government in London for final arbitration. No one, it seems, thought it remotely odd that, for example, the siting of a signal box on the dusty plains of India should ultimately be decided by a solemn conference of Members of Parliament, whose previous experience of railways had been limited to journeys on the London to Brighton line.

Fortunately there were saner voices to be heard in the land. If there was more than a touch of the ludicrous in the deliberation of the supposedly practical men who devised the system of railway construction in India, there is an equally absurd touch to the fact that these good commercial men had to be rescued by Sir James Andrew Brown Ramsey, first Marquess and tenth Earl of Dalhousie, who was appointed Governor General of India in 1847 at the age of thirty-five. He was, at least, aware of the problems presented by a rapidly expanding rail system for he had been Vice-President of the Board of Trade in the Peel administration during the boom years of the 1840s. He was a short, stocky man who managed to combine aristocratic hauteur with bustling energy and a fierce temper. He was an aristocrat by temperament, a man who never for a moment doubted his right as well as his ability to lay down the law for others. He did not suffer fools gladly – nor indeed did he suffer them at all. A splendid example of Dalhousie at work came when he was asked to arbitrate on the experimental line from Calcutta. Around £1 million had been allocated to the East Indian Railway to build a double track to the mines of Raneegunge. For that sum Simms, the company engineer, had calculated that he could either build a single track all the way or a double track that would come to a halt in the middle of nowhere, thirty miles from the mines that were to supply the traffic. The answer might seem obvious, but voices were raised demanding the letter of the law be adhered to and double track must be laid. Dalhousie demolished that argument:

> If the experimental section be constructed in literal conformity with the orders of the Court, of a double line and only so as not to compromise the Government in the slightest degree . . . I conceive that this section, commercially, must be a total failure. If the object . . . is to prove the practicability of forming a railway as a public work, the fact could be proved on a quarter of the distance and at a quarter of the expenses. If, as I have assumed, the object in view is to prove the profitableness as well as the practicability of a railway in India, I regard this proposal as totally useless. The Government might as well contract a railway from the Gaol to the General Hospital.

139

The line was built single track, with space left for a second line to be added at a later date.

Dalhousie's main achievement was to bring rationality and order to railway planning. He had seen at first hand the problems caused in England where Stephenson's standard 4 ft. 8½ inch gauge clashed with Brunel's 7 ft. broad gauge. India was starting with a clean slate: there were no other railways with which connections had to be made, so that a rational decision could be taken and an 'ideal' gauge settled on. Dalhousie put his own views on gauge differences in typically forthright terms: 'The Government of India has in its power, and no doubt will carefully provide that, however widely the railway system may be extended in this Empire in the time to come these great evils should be averted.' So they were, but in less than two decades the pattern was broken. Economy became the new criterion, and the gauge shrank from Dalhousie's proud broad gauge, down past the Stephenson standard, to just one metre. Later these would be joined by an assortment of narrow gauge routes tackling the difficulties of the mountains. But, for a time at least, rationality ruled. Dalhousie's other great contribution was to appoint a Consulting Engineer for Railways in 1850 who was able to take an overall view and lay down sensible rules for development.

Colonel J.P. Kennedy, that fierce denouncer of the piecemeal development of lines in England, established criteria for route selection which never lost sight of the main aim of providing a network of railways that would meet the needs of the whole country. Under Kennedy's guidelines, no one railway was ever considered in isolation but always as part of a greater whole. He made sure that absurd quarrels like that over the East Indian Railway should not recur by laying down that although lines could be built as single track, all earthworks, bridges, tunnels and so forth should be capable of taking a double track. He also set down that the maximum cost per mile of single track should be set at £5000. This was, to say the least, somewhat optimistic. In Britain, up to 1858, the average cost was nearly £35,000 a mile, ranging from £38,000 in England to £115,000 in Ireland. It was estimated that a quarter of that was taken up with the expenses of obtaining an Act and buying land, neither of which was applicable in India, and taking those out of the equation reduces the cost to roughly £26,000. Then again some two thirds of the mileage was double track but even if one makes the very dubious assumption that double track costs twice as much as single, that still produces a figure in excess of £15,000 a mile, or three times Kennedy's allowance. In the event, Kennedy's figure was never achieved, though the Madras Railway did manage to build much of its track at a cost of only £7000 per mile. But the importance of Kennedy's work lay in the fact that standards were set: railway builders knew how matters stood, and on what basis they were expected to operate. Work on the two experimental lines went ahead.

In 1853 an event occurred which the *Overland Telegraph and Carrier* described as 'a triumph, to which in comparison all our victories in the east seem tame and commonplace'. It would, the anonymous enthusiast wrote, 'be remembered by the natives of India when the battlefields of Plassey, Assaye, Meanee and Goojerat have been forgotten'. This was the fact that twenty miles of the Great Indian Railway were opened from Bombay to Thana. Not everyone seemed equally aware of the historic nature of the occasion. It was the habit of the British at the approach of summer to leave the sticky heat of the plain for the comparative cool of the hills. They were not about to change their habits for anything as mundane as the opening of India's first railway. The Governor of Bombay, the Commander-in-Chief and the Bishop of Bombay left for the hills just hours before the ceremony. Was it a deliberate snub? It seems unlikely that it could have been a mere coincidence. The official absence did nothing to dampen the celebrations, as 400 passengers left the Bori Bunde station in Bombay to the accompaniment of a 21-gun salute, the sounding brass of the Governor's band and the cheers of the crowd.

Progress on the eastern line inevitably took longer, and there were some unexpected delays. There was a political row with the French, who still ruled a small parcel of land which they claimed lay directly across the line. For their part the British declared the route was nowhere near any French territory. This was little more than an irritation: the French were in no position to push any claims in India. By 1853 the line had reached Pundooah, 38 miles from Calcutta. All that was needed for a grand inauguration ceremony was a train: unfortunately, a train was just what they did not have. 'Pattern carriages' had been sent over from England, but the ship carrying them sank in the mouth of the Hooghly River. John Hodgson, the Locomotive Chief Engineer, was not unduly concerned. He designed his own carriages and had them manufactured locally. The first locomotives were ordered from Kitson Thompson and Hewitson of Leeds. They were handsome 2-2-2 Well Tank locomotives, with shiny high domes and tall chimneys: one of the class, the *Fairy Queen of 1855*, has pride of place in the New Delhi railway museum. The first engines, however, were delayed, partly because they were shipped out on a bizarrely long route via Australia. As a result the first train only ran in June 1854. The great opening ceremony, in the presence of Dalhousie, took place in 1855 when the whole line was open to Raneegunge. It was not strictly true to say that the line ran from Calcutta. Howrah station, a makeshift affair of huts and sheds, stood across the wide Hooghly river, and passengers from Calcutta had to take a ferry to reach it. Many years were to pass before the river was bridged and the lines reached the city itself.

The experimental railways were an undoubted success and confounded the experts by at once attracting a busy passenger trade. One other line was begun in Madras in Southern India, which opened its first section with equal success in 1856. Railway building, however, was overshadowed and temporarily obliterated by events. The forceful Dalhousie left India in 1856 and his place was taken by the more thoughtful and deliberate Lord Canning, son of a more famous father. Within a year there was a general uprising through most of northern India against British rule, which Indian historians refer to as the War of Independence and which the British of the time gave the equally untrue title of the Mutiny. It was unquestionably a major conflict, which caught up a number of hapless railway builders in its violence.

Those sections of railway that had been built, notably the steadily expanding East India line, the route between Agra and

Delhi and that between Allahabad and Cawnpore, were used by troops, but elsewhere construction sites were attacked and half-completed lines ripped up. The civilian engineers were inevitably drawn into the conflict: some died and those who survived usually joined one of the volunteer forces. The engineers working in small groups far from home base were most at risk: one group only escaped with their lives by hiding out in a newly completed water tower. Some of the most dramatic events occurred in the little town of Arrah between Allahabad and Patna. This was a section of the East India line, but isolated from the railhead which was still stuck at Raneegunge. The engineer in charge, Richard Vicars Boyle, had earlier had a number of skirmishes with local tribesmen, and the tensions that were to build up to the great explosion of the Mutiny itself were already being felt. A small group of engineering staff and their families lived in a European enclave, and long before serious trouble broke out, Boyle arranged for all the wives and children to be sent to the comparative safety of Dinapore, nearly 30 miles away down the line. At the same time he asked for armed protection and the District Magistrate sent a detachment of fifty Sikh police to Arrah.

Boyle was meanwhile making his own arrangements for defence. A small building in the garden, surrounded by a colonnade, was used in more peaceful times as a billiard room. Now Boyle bricked in the arches to create a miniature fort which was ready by mid-July 1857 when the 2500 sepoys at Dinapore rose up and joined the Mutiny. Within two days they descended on Arrah, where they broke into the gaol and raided the treasury before turning their attention to Boyle and his tiny force. They had a small amount of artillery in the form of two light guns, one of which was hauled up to the roof of Boyle's house from where they began firing at the little fortress in the garden. They kept up the bombardment for seven days, during which a relief force was ambushed and routed with heavy casualties. A second relief column under Major Eyre was more circumspect, rounded the flank of the mutineers and scattered them. Boyle and his men survived, and only one of the Sikhs had serious injuries. The incident had no affect on Boyle's career:

he stayed on in India building railways until 1864.

The Mutiny was bloody but short. There was one lasting effect: it marked the end of rule by the East India Company. The change of government had no marked affect on everyday affairs and life, including railway building, gradually went back to normal. There was, however, a new impetus given to construction: if the Mutiny did nothing else it proved the importance of good communications in a vast country. There were also more lasting memorials. New stations became potential fortresses. They all but enclosed the tracks, so that trains could be protected inside. The face these stations presented to the outside world was grim: high walls, rounded corners that would deflect shot, battlemented towers and firing slits. The grander stations, such as Lahore, looked more like medieval castles than places to purchase tickets. But the station-fortresses were not needed. Railway engineers found themselves facing different enemies: a fierce landscape, extremes of weather and the ravages of disease. Contractors also faced their own special problem: prices that had been negotiated before the Mutiny began to look distinctly less appealing afterwards. Among those who came to India was Thomas Brassey who formed a new partnership of Brassey and Wythes for the occasion, and ended up losing money. There was hence an understandable nervousness among European staff in the aftermath of war.

In 1856 John Brunton was appointed chief engineer for the Scinde Railway that was planned to join Karachi to the East Indian Railway at Delhi. The only advice he was given as he left England was to drink soda instead of the local water. It was not a comfortable journey: first by boat to Alexandria, then by camel train to the Red Sea, and on by boat again. The book which he wrote, he said, to amuse his grandchildren, contains accounts of such merry events along the way as the chasing of a giant rat which he killed with his bare hands – of such stuff were Empire Builders made. He arrived at Karachi just as the Mutiny was ending and set about organizing a trip to view the proposed route, or to be more precise he got his Goan butler to organize the trip, since at this stage of his career Brunton had no local languages.

He and his staff set off on camels, camping along the way with
the aid of twelve tent-pitchers. It was the tent pitchers who set
the pace, for they travelled on foot carrying all the gear. Progress
was a modest ten miles a day. Brunton armed himself with a brace
of pistols and a sword, but they were only needed once, not
against rebellious Indians but against a rabid wolf that attacked
a village where they were resting. Five days out, there was an
alarming report that the mutiny had broken out again in Karachi.
Brunton had left his wife there, and he at once grabbed a camel
and galloped through the night on the 56-mile journey back. The
rumour was false, Karachi was calm. He returned to the survey
party at a more sedate pace.

Confidence grew that the peace would last, though there was
no shortage of problems to keep Brunton busy. On the whole
work proceeded smoothly, with the line divided into sections,
each under the control of an assistant engineer. Actual construction was limited to the winter months: in the heat of summer they
caught up on drawing plans and sections. It was still received
wisdom that work should be let to British contractors, even if
those contractors chose to use native labour. One contractor
named Bray aroused suspicion from the start. 'I and my staff',
wrote Brunton, 'had much to do in watching these proceedings
and trying to keep Bray right.' They were not vigilant enough:
Bray absconded taking his funds with him, and leaving the men
unpaid. They were 'a very rough lot' from Central Asia and
rioting broke out, not surprisingly since the men were half-
starved. Brunton seized all the plant and equipment, persuaded
the government to pay the wages bill and decided that in future
he could do without the services of a contractor. They worked
a piece-rate or a day-rate system and gave no more trouble.

Health was a perpetual problem for most Europeans in India.
One particular spot, Darbaji, had been chosen as a site for a station, but no one seemed able to work there for any length of time
without falling ill. Brunton asked a native to show him where the
drinking water came from: 'He took me about ½ a mile into the
Jungle and showed me a small pond of water, covered with green
slime and filth – for the Buffaloes & other animals grazing in the

145

Jungles came here to drink.' He carried out a simple geological survey, sank a well and the problem was solved.

His later career was certainly varied. After the Scinde line was completed a new one was proposed along the Indus valley, to complete the link from Karachi to Multan and the Punjab and Delhi Railway. To some extent, his work was much like that of other engineers surveying in India. He set off with a retinue of thirty-five servants and tent-pitchers, and an escort of fifty cavalry and fifty infantry. One problem Brunton faced was finding suitable stone for ballast, but he had heard of the great ruined city of Brahminabad in the Scinde desert and set out to hunt for it. He found it – surrounded by walls 20 feet thick and 14 feet high: all the ballast an engineer could want provided he had no thoughts for archaeology. During this period, in order to make life more tolerable in Karachi, he ordered 800 tons of ice from the Wenham Lake Ice Company – who sent it to Bombay by mistake. So Brunton bought refrigeration equipment and made his own. Encouraged by this success he then began manufacturing soda water!

When the survey was completed he was called back to England to give evidence in the case of Bray, the absconding contractor – a case that was to drag on for two years. Brunton did not wait for the result but returned to the Indus. In an account which he wrote for the Institution of Civil Engineers, Brunton expressed his opinion of Bray with a dry humour:

Without entering into a statement of the causes of Messrs. Bray's relinquishing the works, which at present form a subject of legal reference, it will suffice to say, that when the Company's Engineers took possession of them, they had to encounter difficulties which were not due entirely to the peculiarities of the country.

As work progressed, the company decided to provide an alternative form of transport, and Brunton found himself with a new job in charge of steamship operations between Kotri, near Hyderabad, and Multan. The steamer was sent out in sections and assembled on the spot, but had difficulty coping with the swift Indus current. It struggled upstream to make the 700-mile journey in thirty-four days; then turned round and shot downstream in a week.

Engineers working overseas were expected to show versatility. John Brunton's spell in charge of river traffic must have been a success, for he was asked to serve for a time as traffic manager on the Indus Valley Railway. His notes on the experience speak volumes on his attitude towards the people amongst whom he lived and worked:

It was at first thought that it would be difficult to get the natives to travel together in the same carriages on account of caste prejudices, but this proved a delusion. An hour before the time of a train starting, crowds of natives surrounded the booking office clamouring for tickets, and at first there was no keeping them to the inside of the carriages. They clambered up on the roofs of the carriages and I have been obliged to get up on the roofs and whip them off. Females were not allowed to travel in the same carriages as the men. A special carriage was allotted for them and I assure you the noise they made in chattering or rather screaming to one another rendered the identification of their particular carriage quite easy. The men travelling, always carry a roll of bedding with them, and besides they always sat cross legged on the seats, so I took out the seats of the 3rd Class carriages and they then squatted on their bundles on the floor of the carriage and thus economized space.

The early pioneering routes had proved their worth, but their true value could only be realized when they linked up with other sections of the developing system. The East Indian Railway had the simpler task, running over level plains (an idea of the terrain can be gained from the fact that in 1338 miles there was only one tunnel built and that was a modest 300 yards). It was not, however, free of problems. The route had to cross numerous rivers that were mere trickles in the dry season but became torrents thousands of feet across in the wet. The lines were continued on past the rivers long before the viaducts were completed. Temporary lines could be laid over the dry river bed, to be replaced by a ferry service in the wet season. James Meadows Rendel, the consultant engineer, turned to a type of bridge that had only recently been tried in Britain, the Warren truss, first used at London Bridge Station in 1850. It was built up of a series of triangular components, and it was a system well adapted for manufacture and testing in England for shipment overseas. Rendel was certainly impressed:

The principle of this bridge has much to recommend it for India. Composed wholly of wrought iron, in comparatively small parts and every part fitted in its place by machinery . . . the ease with which it can be fixed together and taken to pieces again without the slightest injury admits of it being proved in the workshop of the manufacturer, and of it being erected in its permanent position by the most unskilled and indifferent class of mechanics.

The viaducts were very impressive. Four were built to the pattern first seen in Robert Stephenson's high-level bridge at Newcastle-upon-Tyne: a double-decker construction with railway on the top deck and road traffic on the lower. The grandest of these crossed the river Soane in twenty-eight spans, each of 150 feet; the Jumma was only slightly less impressive with a total length of over 3000 feet. The individual parts were made in England, the first coming from Charles Mare's of Blackwall.

The most difficult river crossings were not, however, here but in the Punjab – not so much on the Punjab Railway itself which ran from Amritsar to Multon, but on the Punjab Northern State Railway from Lahore to Jhelum. The only real difficulty experienced on the Punjab Railway was that of getting a locomotive there in the first place. The first delivery was by boat to Ravi, up river from Karachi, and from there the journey overland was like some grand, spectacular procession: 102

bullocks were employed to pull and two elephants came behind to push. The Northern Punjab, however, had to cross three great rivers, including the Chenab. At the point where the railway was to cross, the river had already run for 300 miles, down from the mountains of Kashmir on its way to the Indus still 400 miles away. In its long journey, the river had picked up vast quantities of alluvial soil which had silted to depths of hundreds of feet, so there was no possibility of finding a solid foundation for the piers; and there had to be a great many piers for the river was crossed in sixty-four spans. The bridge was eventually constructed by sinking wells and building the piers on top of them.

The first stage was to construct groynes to divert the river so that a small sandy island was created. A circular kerb of wood was built, with a wedge-shaped cross-section, and laid on the sand as a base for the wall. The circular wall was then built up of brick on top of the kerb, and when it reached a height of about 12 feet, workmen clambered inside and began scooping away the sand so that the brick cylinder gradually began to sink under its own weight. When only a foot of brickwork showed above the surface, another 12 feet of brickwork was built on top of the first and the whole process repeated. As more and more bricks were added and the well sank ever deeper, so friction began to slow the sinking and literally hundreds of tons of rails had to be piled on top. The great danger the workmen faced was that of hitting quicksand, which could flow up through the tube and engulf them. When the well had reached the required depth it was plugged with concrete and filled with sand. Further stability was achieved by dumping concrete blocks round the walls – some 15,000 were made in situ. This immense operation was repeated over and over again, with three wells being sunk for each pier. Then the piers had to be protected from the ravages of the river which could scour up to 50 feet of sand away in one of its frequent floods. Boulders were stacked round the foot of the piers, but unfortunately no suitable stone was available locally. It had to be brought down river on cumbersome rafts that frequently overturned in the dangerous rapids. Finally there stood a bridge twice as grand as any on the East Indian – it was a full mile and three quarters long.

A similar technique was used on the Empress Bridge carrying the Indus Valley State Railway across the Sutlej. This was a vast project with a huge workforce. A shanty town, protected by, as it turned out, inadequate flood banks grew up, which at one time held up to 6000 inhabitants. The engineer, James Bell, noted that once again the workforce suffered appallingly from disease:

> In the worst season it was not uncommon for three men out of four to be laid up simultaneously with fever; and one year when a flood had broken into the place, one thousand workmen are believed to have died of pneumonia.

The difficulties faced on the East Indian were real enough but they seemed minor compared with those confronting the engineers of the Great Indian Peninsula Railway (GIPR). If it was to be extended inland then a way had to be found up the Ghats. Advice was available from the consultant engineer in England, Robert Stephenson, but the principal work of finding and building the route fell to the men on the spot, the Chief Engineer, James Berkley and the engineer who was to supervise the first line, Robert Graham. In the event there were to be two routes up the cliffs that rise to a height of 2500 feet: the first up Thul Ghat, the second up Bhore Ghat. The routes followed inclines at fierce gradients that ranged from 1 in 48 to 1 in 37, and these were no minor affairs: the Thul incline was slightly more than 9 miles long, the Bhore $15\frac{1}{2}$. Both involved the construction of bridges, massive embankments and tunnels, but their most distinctive feature was the zigzag route they took up the cliffs. This was achieved by including reversing stations, so that trains could crawl up the slope along the face of the cliffs to the station, then change direction and continue on, climbing in the opposite direction.

A huge workforce was required for construction. There was an early insistence on importing British navvies, but the men who could perform prodigious feats in northern climates were generally unable – and unwilling – to cope with the tropics. The ones that were brought some of their old habits with them. C.O. Burge

150

described a rowdy crowd carousing on the Madras line. The native policemen tried to restore order, but with little success: 'each navvy took two constables, one under each arm, and chucked them outside the railway fence.' Some stayed on as overseers and gangers, and a number were to be found on the GIPR. Sir Bartle Frere was concerned about the situation and issued an edict that any European striking a native should be instantly dismissed and would forfeit his return fare which had been paid by the company. This news did not percolate down to the men on the ground. On an inspection of the works, he met a 'big brawny navvy' who was in charge of a native gang.

'Well, my good man, you appear to be the manager here.'
'Yes Sir,' was the reply.
'And how are you getting on?'
'Oh, Sir, we are getting on very well.'
'How many natives have you under your orders?'
'Well Sir, about 500 on 'em altogether.'
'Do you speak their language?'
'No Sir I don't.'
'Well then, how do you manage to let these natives understand what they are to do?'
'Oh Sir I'll tell you. I tell these chaps three times in good plain English, and then if they don't understand that, I takes the lukri [the stick] and we get on very well.'

Further enquiries revealed that this navvy was in fact far from being the ogre he claimed to be, but was 'a most kind hearted fellow, much loved by the natives under his charge, who would do anything for him.'

The Bhore Ghat represented an immense labour, with a rise of over 2000 feet, 25 tunnels and 22 bridges. As many as 40,000 were set to work and they suffered terribly, with nearly a third dying from disease. It was not just the labourers who were affected. Solomon Tredwell sailed from England to take a major contract, arriving at Bombay on 15 September 1855. By 30 September he had succumbed to fever and died. That was not the end of the contract. His widow, Alice Tredwell, simply took over and saw it through to completion. It was a daunting task, as the engineer Berkley admitted when he described the problems of gathering together a workforce:

This great force has not been collected without considerable trouble; it is not entirely supplied by the local districts, but is gathered from distant sources. Labourers sometimes tramp for work as in England, and on the same work may be seen men from Lucknow, Guzerat, and Sattara. The wants of the works have, however, been supplied by unusual exertions in sending messengers in all directions, and by making advances to muccadums, or gangers, upon a promise to join the work with bodies of men at the proper season. Country artisans and skilled labourers have their own methods of doing work, but are capable of improvement and are not averse to change their practice. For operations requiring physical force, the low-caste natives who eat flesh and drink spirits, are the best; but for all the better kinds of workmanship, masonry, bricklaying, carpentry, for instance, the higher castes surpass them. Miners are, on the whole, the best class in the country. The natives strictly observe their caste regulations, yet will readily fall into an organisation upon particular works, to which they will faithfully adhere, and in which they are by no means devoid of interest. Although they cling closely to their gangers, they will attach themselves to those European inspectors who treat them kindly. The effective work of almost every individual labourer in India, falls far short of the result obtained in England.

The account is interesting for the light it throws on attitudes. It could seem from reading this account that the ravages of cholera – it killed literally tens of thousands of workers – were chiefly notable for the delays they caused in the works. The account, in fact, raises more questions than it answers. It continues:

The fine season of eight months is favourable for Indian railway operations, but on the other hand, fatal epidemics, such as cholera and fever, often break out and the labourers are, generally, of such a feeble constitution, and so badly provided with shelter and clothing, that they speedily succumb to those diseases, and the benefits of the fine weather are, thereby, temporarily lost.

But why were the local navvies so badly fed and housed? The answer is that they had low pay because they could not perform as well as the British navvy. And the reason for this was partly that they were badly fed and housed and hence prone to disease. They were caught in a circle of poverty from which, it seems, there was no escape. The Europeans who employed them were not callous monsters, but followers of the rules that governed behaviour in England as closely as it did in India. It was the duty of the employer to pay no more than was absolutely necessary, otherwise the economy of the country would have been thrown into chaos: 'It has enabled the Company to draw largely and advantageously upon the resources of the country, both in labour and materials, without suddenly, or unduly affecting the public markets.' The attitudes that permeate the thinking of those who came to build railways for the great Indian Empire are, not surprisingly, those of conventional Victorian England. They congratulated themselves for not disturbing the labour market and, at the same time, encouraging the spirit of entrepreneurship among a developing Indian middle class. There was general satisfaction at the success of one Indian contractor, as Berkley noted:

A Parsee contractor, Mr. Jamsetjee Dorabjee, has executed four main-line contracts as satisfactorily, as expeditiously, and as cheaply, as any of the European firms, and is now about completing his fifth, which comprises some of the heaviest works on the lines.

The railway company was a microcosm of British India. There was a willingness to encourage 'the best' of the Indians, combined with a deep-seated belief that the native could never be expected to take control of his own affairs. The guiding hand would be European.

The Company's Engineers, Assistant Engineers, and Surveyors are generally Europeans, but one native Engineer has won his way to the office of Assistant Engineer, and has skilfully discharged its duties for three years. In the office establishment of draftsmen, accountants and clerks, all the situations have been held by natives. As inspectors of work, natives have been chiefly employed. As district inspectors of the line, when opened, native agency is already partially adopted, and is, by encouragement, gradually becoming more useful. The principle to be kept in view is, that only by means of European and native co-operation, can the great railway undertakings which are required in the Bombay Presidency, be accomplished with due despatch. European skill, experience, and management, are of primary importance, but native agency has proved much more valuable and efficient than was anticipated, and will, undoubtedly, be found capable of considerable and rapid growth, if it is adopted without prejudice, and is treated with equity; and if native employees of all classes are stimulated to improve themselves, by the assurance of their gradual advancement, according to merit.

Yet the belief that Europe knows best was to lead to absurdities. Material was sent to India that was already available locally. For instance, creosoted sleepers were shipped out from England many of which by the time they reached the workings were split and useless. More incongruous was the use of wholly inappropriate technologies. India was not short of local building materials or of building expertise – how could anyone who had seen the great cities and temples of the Moghul Empire believe that it was? Yet it was still thought to be sensible to prefabricate booking halls and engine sheds and ship them to India. And what material was used for these buildings? Iron! Could anyone have

154

seriously believed that an iron building was appropriate for a waiting room in the blistering heat of an Indian summer? Apparently they could and did. Fortunately for the future of Indian railways, there were others who realized that Indian methods had developed that were appropriate to the land and its climate and that the best results were likely to be obtained by combining the traditions of the East with the new technology of the West. It is worth quoting Berkley at length in a description of working methods where he explained how he eventually discovered that 'some Indian modes of doing work, which seemed barbarous and clumsy, were the cheapest and quickest means which could be employed.' He starts, however, with the negative side of working in India, where techniques were previously wholly unknown. Tunnelling provided an excellent example.

> The whole process, except blasting and excavation, was unknown to native workmen. In the earliest tunnels, where the top was heavy, it was found, at first, impossible to keep native miners in the heading, and the timbering was done chiefly by Europeans and one or two Parsee carpenters, and the arch was keyed in by the former alone. Native miners use the churn drill, with which they are very handy, and they have sometimes been brought to work in pairs with the hammer, and strike with dexterity. They will work hard in close contact, and in the foulest atmosphere. They are careless in blasting operations, and consequently, the loss of life has been considerable; miners have been seen to fire a shot with a bamboo, and lie upon the ground while it exploded.

On the other hand when it came to more conventional building the old methods were shown to be perfectly satisfactory.

> In staging and scaffolding it is only rarely, and in very large works, that the English example has been followed, nor are crabs and derricks so often met with as might be expected. The reason for this is afforded by experience, which has taught how cheap and expeditious it sometimes is, to use the

155

native process. The bamboo coolies, or carriers of heavy weights, will lift their loads up the roughest staging and the masons and labourers require but little help, to find their way to the work at the top of the highest piers. The centering commonly adopted in the country, was to fill up the arch with stone and earth, and to shape the top to the form of the soffit, or at other times, to use almost a forest of jungle wood in scaffolding a rough centre. For these, centres of English construction have invariably been substituted, with, as may be conceived, immense advantage to the work.

Even today, quite sophisticated building sites in India can only be glimpsed through a thicket of bamboo scaffolding that looks to the uninitiated as if it needs no more than a mosquito to alight on one corner for the whole complex structure to topple to the ground. Yet it is a system which has, literally, stood the test of time.

It was not by any means always, or even usually, the fault of Indian contractors and workmen when things went wrong. Robert Maitland Brereton came to India to work on the GIPR in 1856 and his greatest difficulty lay with the European contractors and their poor, skimped work. Cement was left out in the sun, and instead of being regularly soaked was allowed to dry out and was then simply layered between stones in the form of a useless crumbling mass. Stone piers were supposed to be held together by 'binders', long stones that run the whole width of the structure to give added strength: these were simply left out and the stone which looked so fine was no more than an outer cladding. On one contract, No. 12, a score of viaducts and bridges collapsed. Brereton himself detected sharp practice on another contract and issued a critical report. He was inspecting other examples of the same contractor's handywork when he was almost laid out by a blow on the head. He had just enough time to see the contractor's agent wielding the stick. Brereton's lip remained resolutely stiff: 'I did not condescend, in the presence of the native workmen, to assault him in return, but quietly wrote out on a leaf of my pocket book an order for him to stop all masonry work.' But whatever the problems met by the engineers, contractors and workmen, the GIPR, with its spectacular ascent of the Ghats, remains one of the great triumphs of nineteenth-century civil engineering.

For the young engineers who came out from Britain, India was an exotic experience and a challenge. C.O. Burge came from Ireland in the 1860s to work, or so he expected, as assistant engineer on the Madras Railway. His arrival was exciting enough. There was no harbour at Madras, so he came ashore in a 'masula boat', an alarmingly flimsy looking vessel about 40 feet long made of bamboo and leather. This was to carry him in through the surf. The boatmen hovered on the swell, picked a likely looking wave and headed for shore.

The momentum carries the masula boat high and dry on to the bank, when all the occupants who do not hold on like an attack of influenza are thrown into a jumble of boxes and portmanteaus, so that the astonished traveller is literally hurled into India.

He reported for duty and found he had arrived a fortnight before the rest of the young engineers were expected. So, on a simple first-come-first-served principle, he was promptly put in charge of an entire section – leaping up several rungs of the promotional ladder in one jump. He then went up country, an experience which constituted a crash course in self-sufficiency. The first stage of his journey was by train, and where the tracks ended he continued on horseback, his luggage and few sticks of furniture slowly trundling along by bullock cart. He stopped at simple guest bungalows or the homes of his fellow engineers spread out along the line, until he reached his section, nearly 40 miles from his nearest fellow-European colleague. It was the custom for the engineering staff to build their own bungalows, but common sense dictated that local practices were followed. Houses were generally built with a verandah all the way round providing shade in the summer and protecting the building from the downpours of the monsoons. Burge's predecessor had scorned precedent and built a verandah along one side of the building

157

only. The monsoons came, the rain lashed at the exposed walls, washing away the mud that held the stones in place, and the whole place came crashing down. Burge rebuilt it – in traditional style.

He solved the problem familiar to other engineers in winter, the rivers that could turn overnight from trickles to waterways three times the width of the Thames in London. He learned to improvise. Temporary tracks were laid across river beds in the dry season, which were used not just for construction purposes but for regular passenger services as well. Above all, he learned to delight in the mixture of racial types, men and women, who made up his workforce. Because of a local labour shortage, he found himself employing workers from all over India including Afghans and Pathans who arrived with alarmingly long, sharp knives stuck in their belts. 'Their features, or sometimes the absence of them showed that they usually settled their differences by private enterprise without troubling Government legal machinery.' Some learned English, but inevitably produced the occasional howler. Three men appeared with a note which read, 'Sir – herewith I have the honour to enclose three bricklayers'. And official documents combined the starchy language of bureaucracy with startling outbursts of colloquialism: 'I have the honour to inform you that Mootheswamy and Soobarou have booted it on Friday last, and I have replaced them by two good masons.' Men like Burge enjoyed India and served the country well. They were not always so well served themselves.

In 1868, Robert Brereton was appointed chief engineer for the Calcutta and Nagpur line. He picked his own staff and was confident enough to tell the Board he would have the work finished by May 1870, eighteen months ahead of schedule. He drove the storekeepers mad, harrying them for materials. One of the main sources of delay on a good many lines was lack of even the basic materials – so that gangs would be sent around with, for example, a full stock of rails and sleepers but no chairs. Brereton made sure this never happened. He also followed the American practice of laying temporary track over obstacles, ranging from rivers to gulleys, to keep his supply lines open. Even so, there were some elements over which he had no control. In 1869, cholera came to the Nerbudda valley: hundreds died and workmen fled from the area. Brereton himself succumbed and was lucky to survive. In spite of this, the line was ready as promised, at which point the successful engineer was given his notice with not so much as a thank you.

The railways discussed so far were all built as part of the usual process of establishing a rail network for a country that would carry the people and commerce of a nation. In India, other considerations came into play: some railways were built primarily to meet military rather than civil needs. The outbreak of the Afghan wars in the 1870s brought a new urgency to the need to provide rails to the troubled North-West Frontier. The result was the Kandahar Railway which was planned to run from Sukkur on the Indus, a spot which could be supplied by barges and steam tugs, north to Kandahar, actually across the old Indian frontier in Afghanistan. The first stage was only to run from Sukkur to the entrance of the Bolan Pass through the mountains. That presented problems enough. First came the broad plain, criss-crossed by hundreds of irrigation channels, then 40 miles of dense jungle, followed by the greatest challenge of all, 94 miles of 'dry, barren, treeless plain' crossed by spill channels that would remain empty for years on end, then quite suddenly be filled to overflowing by flash floods. The natural difficulties were, by any standards, bad enough but construction was made doubly difficult by the demands of time.

There was no time to arrange for special supplies to meet the needs of the builders – any kind of rail or sleeper that was available had to be used. An extraordinary collection of hardware was soon accumulating on site. By sea from Bombay came enough rails for 50 miles of track, but sleepers for only 25; and even the rails were a mixture of new ball-headed steel and worn-out track uprooted from heaven knows where. Other lines rendered up an equally bizarre mixture of pot-sleepers, double-headed chair roads and flat-footed track – and even that could be sub-divided into many different types. Somehow all had to be put together by an inexperienced workforce to make a coherent whole. It could only work if a strict set of rules was laid down, so that the right sleepers finished up fastened by the right chairs to the right rails. The secret lay in organization: each train was to be marshalled so that rails came first, fastenings second, then sleepers. It never worked. Each train was a higgledy-piggledy mess of trucks that even after hours of shunting disgorged material that then had to be sorted by hand. The best drilled gangs in the world would have been hard pressed to make sense of this chaos; and the builders of the Kandahar Railway were not blessed with the best drilled gangs. Every time a new type of track had to be laid it was as if the whole job was being started again from scratch. It was, as the engineer James Bell's reports make clear, all very frustrating.

For instance, a man might be employed one day on boring sleepers and spiking the flat-footed rail, and the next day he would be thrown out of work on the commencement of the pot-road, until he could be taught to fit and cotter tie-bars to pots, set the pots out for the linkers, or drive keys.

It was an administrative nightmare. Just as difficult a problem was presented by the logistics of getting material moved on the last lap of the journey to the advancing railhead. Here local technology took over and proved itself to combine practicality, cheapness and a degree of sophistication. The engineer responsible for much of the work, George Moyle, described the arrangements for supplying the plate-layers:

This was done by bullock-carts, a fair number of which were obtainable in the districts through which the line passed. These carts cost complete but £1 10s., they are easily and readily repaired, and are constructed to travel over roads of the roughest description. They are built of rough-hewn jungle wood. One end of the wooden axle, which revolves, is square, and the other round, so that one wheel is fixed on the axle, and the other loose; this arrangement enables the carts to be turned about very easily. To enable these carts to be used, service roads had to be constructed on each side

160

of the line, and carried over the numerous canals on rough
timber, or floating bridges.

The materials were not the only problem: men had to be looked
after as well. The original idea had been to make up a long train
of wagons, each equipped with an awning, which when shunted
together would make a crude tent some four hundred feet long.
This was not popular, but the camping train did provide a service
as mobile shop, hospital, stores shed and treasury. The men
preferred their own solution:

For housing primarily the earthwork men and ultimately the
platelayers, the surveyors began the erection of temporary
sheds of reed mats at every 6 miles. But as they could not
get enough camels or carts to carry out the mats, only two
such camps were constructed. The plate-laying labourers
took kindly to the mat-work sheds, and as the temper of the
men was too precarious to warrant much interference with
their predilections, the sheds were continually rebuilt at
every 3 miles, and kept about one hundred men employed
on their erection, while the renewals of mats and bamboos
(about a wagon load in every train) occupied carrying capacity that could ill be spared. The mats were each about 4 feet
6 inches square. A single row of mats on edge formed the
back wall of the shed, and another single row of mats laid
flat formed the roof. The sheds were built with their backs
to the north, and though pervious to wind and rain, they
broke the force of the wind so as to make it safe for men
provided with blankets to sleep under them so long as it did
not rain.

Rain was certainly not the problem; water supply as the lines
approached the desert was. A reservoir was established at the
furthest point of the canal system, but beyond that water tanks
had to be sent out by train every day. Perhaps the greatest difficulty of all was in persuading men to come and work in the
desert, even when the arrangements for water supply were

explained. This is not too surprising. The climate was vicious – a boiling hot day could be followed by a night so cold that ice formed on the water barrels. Other sections presented their own unique problems to the administrators, and the jungle in particular seemed to have been specially designed to create an environment where chicanery could thrive:

> Throughout 45 miles the line passed through heavy jungle, which afforded excellent cover to such drivers as desired to decamp with their bullocks, shirk work, or free themselves of their load. To prevent such irregularities, it was found necessary to post patrols of irregular cavalry on both sides of the line, and along the main roads by day, and by night to form the carts into a laager presided over by sentries.

The demand on the carts was immense. It was estimated that every mile of track laid needed 600 carts. The bulk of the traffic was made up of rails, 500 per mile but only 2 per cart, and sleepers, 1600 at 8 per cart load. The wonder is that the line got built at all.

At this time the military were not entirely given over to their more obvious tasks, nor were they notably less imaginative than their civilian counterparts. R.E. Crompton was an officer in the Rifle Brigade, but steam engines were his passion. He built a small steam carriage while still at school but his boldest experiment was reserved for India. That railways were infinitely better than the bullock carts, swaying and creaking down every Indian road, was beyond dispute – but did they have to be *rail*ways? Why not build a steam engine to travel on the common roads? He proposed a 'Government Steam Train' to run on the newly improved Grand Trunk Road that stretched out northwards from Delhi. The engines were ordered from Ipswich, and one of these, *Ravee*, showed its mettle by outpacing a good train, on the adjoining railway. Crompton wrote, enthusiastically, 'though our loaded train weighed over forty tons, we were making speeds well over twenty – probably nearer thirty – miles an hour.' The Government Steam Train had a brief, but not inglorious, career.

Most military endeavour was bent towards more serious ends, and military engineers were to face some of the sternest challenges India could present.

Work had stopped on the Kandahar Railway long before the final objective had been reached simply because the political climate had changed and it was no longer diplomatic to continue it. Then in the 1880s Russia again began to make aggressive noises and the old North-West Frontier manoeuvres began as if nothing had happened to interrupt them. The railway that had been declared wholly unnecessary a decade earlier was now an essential supply line. Diplomacy, however, was not yet ready to admit to a complete volte face – surveyors were sent out to work on the Harnai Road Improvement Scheme. There was no mention of the fact that this particular road was to be improved by the laying of steel rails. It was a feeble pretence, and the route soon had a new name: the Sind Peshin State Railway.

The military engineer's view was uncompromising:

The line does not wind its way through smiling valleys to the breezy heights above. It traverses a region of arid rock without a tree or a bush and with scarcely a blade of grass – a country in which Nature has poured out all the climatic curses at her command. In summer the lowlands are literally the hottest corner of the earth's surface, the thermometer registering 124°F in the shade, while cholera rages, although there is neither swamp nor jungle to provide it with a lurking place. In winter the upper passes are filled with snow and the temperature falls to 18° below zero, rendering outdoor labour an impossibility. The few inhabitants that the region possesses are thieves by nature and cut-throats by profession, and regard a stranger like a gamekeeper does a hawk. Food there is none, and water is often absent for miles. Timber and fuel are unknown and, in a word, desolation writ very large is graven on the face of the land.

The line was built through what was, in every sense, hostile territory. The route ran up the Nari River gorge to a station aptly named Tanduri, or 'Oven', where the only water came from a pool mainly inhabited by crocodiles. The line was regularly raided by local tribesmen, but weather and disease proved the more lethal enemies. In 1885 cholera wiped out 2000 of the 10,000 workforce.

In 1887, 19.27 inches of rain were recorded, six times the average. Then there was the terrain. The route climbed inexorably from an altitude of 433 feet at Sibi to a summit of 6537 feet. Quite the most spectacular feature along the route was the Chappar Rift, a gorge with almost vertical rock walls that lay right across the line of the track. The railway circled as though eyeing up the adversary, then dived into a tunnel, to emerge at the very edge of the chasm. Then with one mighty leap in the form of a 233-feet-high bridge it spanned the rift to disappear into another tunnel on the far side. The spot was so inaccessible that no heavy machinery could be brought in and only light drills could be used. Gunpowder and dynamite were used for blasting and the debris was all cleared away by hand. Worse was to come at Mudgorge, a spot that suited its name exactly, a desolate valley with a floor of mud, made up of an unholy mixture of shale, clay and soft stone. It was firm enough in winter but in summer turned into a sea of porridge. Thousands of feet of rail were laid only to be washed away in storms until the engineers finally decided to dig a cutting and cover it over to provide a tunnel secure from the elements. Even then the elements had the last word. In 1942, a flood roared down Chappar Rift washing away rock, scree and the railway. There was no chance of repair: there was nowhere left to put the tracks. The life of the Sind Peshin Railway was ended.

There are other spectacular railways in India. The Darjeeling Himalayan Railway, opened in 1880, climbs from the heat of the plain to the cool of the hills, rising to an altitude of over 7000 feet in 51 miles during the course of which it winds round itself in a series of loops. The most dramatic of these at Agony Point was built with a curve of just 59½ feet radius. It was almost possible for the engine of a long train to be passing on a bridge over its own brake van. Yet even this line never posed the

164

problems set on the Sind Peshin. This was perhaps India's engineers' greatest challenge.

Across the border in Burma, no railway building began until the 1870s when the Rangoon to Prome line was built, largely using convict labour. Military engineers who had been working in India often found themselves being shunted across the border. India provided excellent training for the rigours of Burma. Colonel, later Sir Gordon, Hearn worked in 1899 as surveyor for a line from Mysore to Tellicherry which included that inevitable obstacle facing all west coast lines, the Ghats. In this case they consisted of hills rising to a height of 2000 feet and covered in dense forest. His predecessor, a young officer, had tried to follow a cart track, but that had been no help. The chief engineer, universally known as 'Buff-Puff' Groves, told him to strike out into the forest which numbered among its perils large numbers of lethal pit vipers. The young man said, 'As a family man, I must decline', and went home. Hearn was given the dubious distinction of being appointed in his place. He did not record meeting any of the deadly snakes but he met almost everything else. Wild elephants roamed the forest and during the monsoons which produced the largest proportion of the 400 inches of rain that fall in the area in a year, there was an infestation of leeches. Everyone except Hearn got malaria. And these were just additional problems tacked on to the main task of pushing a line through forest where the trees were up to 150 feet high.

In 1906, Hearn went off to Burma to work on the line from Thazi to the plateau of the southern Shan State. Work had begun two years earlier but Hearn was not happy with the route so he set off as he had in India to walk through the forest. On the first day he covered 18 miles tramping through rough country, until he found a better route through the hills. An extension of the line involved more walking, over 200 miles in three weeks with Burmese assistants. 'The speed with which the Burmans build a shelter for the night made it unnecessary to carry a tent, but they are not industrious workers, and being sensitive to the sun's rays would not toil when the sun was high. In fact, the only sound to be heard at mid-day was a snore!' Noël Coward, it seems, was right about mad dogs, Englishmen and the midday sun. Burma presented very real difficulties to the engineer. Lieutenant Colonel L.E. Hopkins surveyed the line from Mandalay to the Chinese border near Kunlong. It rose steeply from the plain and the first thousand foot climb was so rapid that the route would have had to zigzag with no fewer than four reversing stations. The other engineer working on the same line, Lieutenant W.A. Watts-Jones, had the misfortune to inadvertently wander across the Chinese border and was executed for his mistake. In the event the difficulties proved too great and the line was never built.

India's other near neighbour, Ceylon, proved equally difficult for railway builders. An obvious starting point was the ancient capital of Kandy in the centre of the island to the port of Colombo, the modern capital. A company was set up in 1847, and T. Drone made a survey. Nothing very much happened until 1856 when the government offered guarantees on the Indian pattern, offering to pay 6 per cent on the first £800,000 and 5 per cent on any extra expenditure. Captain W.S. Moorsom who had made his reputation on the very different Chester & Holyhead Railway was asked to report on the plans, and W.T. Doyne was appointed chief engineer. He found so many problems that he had to seek advice from two of the leading engineers of the day, first Robert Stephenson, then Sir John Hawkshaw. Even their combined talents could not solve the difficulties and, beaten, Doyne resigned. He was replaced by G.L. Molesworth who realized that nothing could be done with the original route. He surveyed a new, and altogether better, route, but before work could be started, the contract between the government and the company ran out and a brand new contract was negotiated for the construction with W.F. Faviell. It is easy to see why the engineers took so long to decide on a route, for even Molesworth's improved line contained some hair-raising engineering. The main feature is the Kadugannawa incline, a 12-mile-long slope lifting the line almost 1500 feet to the summit. It winds up the side of the mountains, in places clinging to a ledge scarcely wider than the 5ft. 6 inch-wide tracks with drops of as much as a thousand feet over the edge. It dives through ten tunnels and numerous cuttings blasted

166

out of the rock, and swings in giddy curves. It was opened in 1867.

The next Sinhalese railway, the Kalutan, just under 28 miles long, seemed to offer far fewer difficulties apart from one river crossing. This crossing was to be carried on two lattice girder bridges joined by a short embankment on a central island. Tests had shown that the river bed was gravel, and iron cylinders were lowered into place for the piers. It was only then that the engineers discovered that the 'solid' foundation was no more than two feet thick, and underneath was soft sand. In the event, they had to go down to a depth of 50 feet before they met rock.

One of the most important tasks in Ceylon was the establishment of a transport route that would link the coffee plantations, mostly at an altitude of 3000–3500 feet, with Colombo, for the export market. A line was built out from the first Kandy route as far as Nawalapitiya, and the rest of the journey was on bullock carts on precipitous zigzagging roads. These roads were difficult to make and once made they were equally difficult to maintain. The heavily laden bullock carts had narrow wheels that dug ruts deep into the surface, and the loose surface was then open to the elements. In an area with an average rainfall of 150 inches this spelled serious erosion. The net result was a system where carts seldom travelled more than six miles a day at exorbitant cost. By 1872 the planters had had enough and petitioned for an extension of the railway to Badulla in the heart of the coffee-growing district of Uva.

Work began under the Surveyor General's Department with John Stoddart in charge. Once the preliminary surveys had shown that the project was feasible, full engineering surveys were undertaken, first under Alex Macnair then, from 1877, under James Mosse. It was decided early on that the gradient on the Kadugannawa incline should be maintained, which meant that the maximum gradient for the whole line was set at 1 in 44. This was more easily proposed than achieved. The hills of the district tend to rise up in steep spurs and are separated by deep ravines. Any line was going to have to go round more obstacles than it was to go over. Badulla is only 560 feet above the start at Kandy but to achieve a reasonable grade the line rose by 4600 feet and then fell by 4040 feet – and at 115 miles was twice as long as the old coast routes. Surveying in such conditions was nightmarish. Selecting this circuitous line in the first place was bad enough, but the detailed work was even more difficult.

Ten assistant engineers were appointed and the staff was never more than twelve. Keeping the gradient while at the same time fitting the curves as economically as possible around spur and chasm involved immense labour, and because of the nature of the terrain the engineers had to keep close together. There was never more than a pair working in one party. Mosse described a typical day:

> About 7 a.m. the two engineers accompanied by about twenty-five Sinhalese as chainmen, axemen, &c., left their camp, and after walking for about an hour and a half commenced work and continued at it till noon; they then returned to camp and plotted the work done that morning, so as to see how it would fit into that to be done the next day, a system which was found to be indispensable. For long distances the route lay through heavy jungle, where not more than 10 chains of line could be cut or levelled per day; in fact the progress made by each party did not exceed 1 mile per week. This slow rate of progress was owing to the unusual ruggedness of the country, the tropical and unhealthy climate, the excessive rainfall, varying from 150 to 180 inches per annum, the inexperience of the Sinhalese chainmen, and the difficulty of working through an interpreter. About four years were occupied in making the surveys and preparing plans and estimates for 112 miles of railway.

The actual work of construction was simple by comparison: the surveyors had laid down the line and cleared the way. The contract went to Thomas Newell & Co. who took on the job at the comparatively modest cost of £15,000 per mile. In time the island developed a spider's web of lines, wriggling and jinking their way from Jaffna in the north to Matara in the south.

Far smaller islands than Ceylon were deemed ripe for railway development in the nineteenth century. Mosse was also to be involved in construction on Mauritius out in the Indian Ocean. As it is no more than 36 miles long and 28 miles wide it might not seem a candidate for a railway at all: in fact it got two, the Midland and the Northern. Both were narrow gauge, and both served the sugar plantations. The first survey was authorized in 1858 by the Secretary of State for the Colonies, but attempts to raise private capital failed lamentably. There was nothing like enough money in Mauritius itself, and British investors were none too keen to invest in a dot on the map somewhere east of Madagascar. Eventually the lines were paid for by issuing a million pounds of colonial development bonds. That paid for an impressive team: Hawkshaw was the consultant engineer in England and Brassey and Wythes the contractors. The Midland was the more dramatic of the two lines. Starting at Port Louis in the west it climbed for 16 miles to the summit at a height of 1817 feet then plunged down for 19 miles to Makebourg in the east. Curves were tight and the fiercest gradient was 1 in 27.

Platelayers and engine drivers were hired in England on three-year contracts, with free passage, except for those who were sent home for misconduct. Platelayers got £150 per annum, free accommodation and a £25 bonus if they got a certificate of good conduct. Other workers – carpenters, masons and the 'coolies' who took on most of the hard labour – were employed locally. Mosse was not impressed: 'Slow and not over industrious.' The engine drivers probably had the most interesting time. The first locomotives were 0-6-0Ts from Sharp Stewart, but they were not powerful enough to cope with the hills, so replacements were sent out, 0-6-0 STs with bigger cylinders. One gets some idea of the difficulties faced on the line by the fact that each engine had four sand boxes, filled with sand specially imported from the Cape. Even then they still slipped. The early morning run, when the rails were still wet with dew, had a quarter of an hour added on to the usual time: that meant they were scheduled to complete their journey up to the summit at a spanking 8 m.p.h. Once over the top, they rushed down the other side at a theoretical speed of 15

169

m.p.h. but this was often more like 25 m.p.h. and involved a good deal of braking in carriages and wagons to avoid the engine overheating. There may not have been very much to the Mauritius railway system, but it certainly never lacked interest. It was also opened many years before either of the two Asian giants, China and Japan, joined the railway world.

This position is scarcely surprising. The Europeans who advanced into Asia as empire builders, traders or military leaders found themselves confronted in the Far East with massive, wealthy and united countries in China and Japan. In this respect the similarities between China and Japan far outweighed the differences. The Japanese, in particular, looked at the men of the West and what they had to offer and, like a housewife faced with an over-persistent doorstep salesman, slammed the door. In the 1630s Japan became a *sakoku* or closed country. It remained locked in fuedalism until the middle of the nineteenth century. The county was run by the military caste of the samurai with their leader the shogun as absolute feudal ruler. It was inevitable that such a closed world could not last forever. China and Japan were mighty forces in the seventeenth century, but they remained set in that time while the rest of the world moved on through the convolutions of the Industrial Revolution. The differences wrought by time were given a dramatic demonstration in one of the most infamous chapters in imperial history, the Opium Wars of the 1840s. China had refused to accept opium from India, and Britain in the holy name of 'Free Trade' forced the unholy drug upon them. The supremacy of western armament was there for all to see, and China had no choice: Hong Kong was ceded to Britain and Chinese ports were open to British and European trade. Japan could not remain immune to the changes convulsing her close neighbour. By the 1850s there were strong forces at work in Japan demanding new contacts with the outside world and threatening the despotic powers of the shogun. By the late 1850s, the most important man in Japan was Ii Naosuke who became regent following the death of the childless shogun. He was anti-reform and violently anti-foreigner, but he could not prevent the

170

reverberations of the Opium Wars being felt in Japan. When the Western powers demanded trading rights, he had no option but to grant them. The only alternative was a war that quite clearly he could not win. It was a terrible blow to samurai pride and in 1860 he paid the price when he was cut down by samurai warriors outside Edo castle.

Paradoxically it was the death of Ii Naosuke that brought about exactly what the old brigade most feared. With his death, the forces that had upheld the power of the shogun were fatally weakened. There was a period of conflict and civil war which ended with the establishment of a new ruler, the young emperor Meiji. The new ruler began a process of change that was to convert Japan from a feudal, rural society into a major industrial military power in an astonishingly short time. The facts of the new Japan were dramatically affirmed in 1905. Just as Western supremacy in arms technology had brought about victory in the Opium Wars, now the Japanese fleet was to annihilate that of Russia in the Russo-Japanese War. It had taken no more than four decades to work the transformation.

The Meiji dynasty promoted change and railway construction was high on the list of priorities. It was not an easy matter to arrange. There was still a deep-seated distrust of foreigners, yet foreign expertise was clearly needed. First, plans were laid in 1870 for a trunk route to connect the old capital Kyoto to the new capital of Edo, now renamed Tokyo. This was an ambitious first project, so it was early decided to break it down into more manageable portions, beginning with the sections Tokyo to Yokohama and Kobe to Osaka. In all public pronouncements the role of the Japanese was played up and that of their European advisers either played down or ignored altogether. This was notably true in the case of locomotives. The list of early suppliers contains all the familiar names of British companies – Beyer Peacock, Sharp Stewart, Kitson, Vulcan, Manning Wardle and more. The time eventually came when the Japanese would want to build their own locomotives and they turned to the locomotive superintendent of the western section of the mainline, Richard F. Trevithick.

It is one of the those extraordinary turns of events that the first Richard Trevithick seldom received his due as designer of Britain's first steam locomotive. Now his grandson was to suffer a similar fate in Japan. He not only designed the country's first home-built engine, but he also built the first compound to be seen in Japan. It was wheeled out for its trials in April 1893 and proved an immense success, but as Francis Trevithick sourly noted,

History repeats itself, as Richard Trevithick senior was branded with folly and madness by the late James Watt for bringing into use the high pressure engine, and even not known to the general public as the builder and inventor of the first locomotive; so will Richard Trevithick of Kobe never be known in Japan by the Japanese as the designer and builder of the first locomotive, the credit already given to a Japanese who has very little mechanical knowledge.

The Trevithicks were, however, to stay on in Japan and continued to play an active role in railway development.

Lack of recognition, an air of suspicion among associates and a lack of understanding of Western technology in the early years were to create problems for many British engineers. An engineer who worked in Japan explained the system they adopted:

The Government undertook, with that self-reliance for which the Japanese were celebrated, to carry out the works themselves, instead of employing skilled contractors as had first been intended. They engaged a staff of competent English engineers, and set to work to make their own railways. They dictated their own terms; they stipulated where everyone should go; and the engineers had to lay out the line and to advance the works in the best way they could with such labourers as the country afforded. The duties of the engineers were beset by many difficulties, arising from the jealousy of the natives towards foreigners, their ignorance of the language, and the incompetence of the subordinate

172

native staff, through whom alone their directions could be
given to the artisans and labourers, none of whom had had
any training on public works, and therefore the engineers
had to teach them everything that required to be done.

There is some doubt as to the very first railway to be built in
Japan. A Scots merchant Thomas B. Glover is said to have built
a short line along the waterfront at Nagasaki, but it was at best
a very limited affair. His other claim to fame is that at the
end of the shogun period, he helped to smuggle a group of
progressive-minded young samurai out of the country to study
engineering in London. If that did nothing else it did at least
provide a nucleus of pro-Western engineers. But the real beginning was marked by the arrival of Edmund Morel to take over
the job of chief engineer for the Tokyo to Kyoto line. He faced
a daunting task, as Francis Trevithick pointed out in 1894:

The country is hardly suitable for an extended railway
system. It is volcanic and hilly, the centre being occupied by
ridges whose peaks attain heights of from 7,000 to 10,000
feet and whose spurs extend to the coast. The celebrated
mountain of Fuji, an extinct, or dormant, volcano, is a cone
of 12,365 feet high, in an almost isolated position near the
coast. Rivers are numerous but not of great length. They are
generally subject to violent floods, either in early Summer
from the melting of snow on the mountains, or in Autumn
from general heavy rains. In many places the beds of the
rivers are above the level of the surrounding country, and
the breaking of the banks in flood-time occasions great
destruction of property and ruin of agricultural land by
deposit of sand and gravel.

Morel, however, had just come from railway building in the
equally difficult terrain of New Zealand. His first decision, when
faced with Japanese scenery, was to decide on a narrow gauge of
3ft. 6 inches, which would help in the building by allowing tighter
curves and steeper gradients. Morel was also very particular

about giving encouragement to his young Japanese assistants. Sadly, he died in 1871 at the early age of thirty, just before the first section from Yedo to Yokohama was officially opened by the Mikado in 1872. This did not go quite as planned. The Mikado made a speech thanking Counts Ito, Okuma and Sangi: 'We express our great satisfaction for the undeviating obedience to our will for the introduction of railways, and the overcoming of all opposition and difficulties.' But the elaborate ceremony was still very much under way when Thomas Hart, anxious not to be late, turned up at the regulator of a brand new 2-4-0T from the Vulcan works. The distinguished guests approached the train much as they would if invited anywhere else: at the door they stopped and took their shoes off before getting into the carriages. They were more than a trifle upset to find no shoes awaiting them at the other end.

These early years were largely dominated by British engineers: 94 out of the 104 jobs given to foreigners went to them, largely it was said as belated 'thank you' for those who had started their career in the group smuggled out to study in London. Among them was Edward Holtham who arrived in November 1873 and was to spend eight years working in Japan. He spent three weeks inspecting the Tokyo to Yokohama Railway which turned out to be such a wretched affair that it all had to be rebuilt, a job Holtham was to tackle in 1878. He then went on to Kobe to take over the line to Osaka. 'Engineering in Japan,' he decided, 'is not as it is elsewhere.' Among other absurdities he discovered that where the first tunnel he inspected had been correctly built to take a double track, the next only allowed for single. This he was told was due to 'communication error'. However, he was soon at work himself and experiencing the difficulties of coping with Japan at first hand. He set off from a base in a village on the shore of Lake Biwa to survey a route through the hills. The going was tough, involving a good deal of tree-felling for sight lines and winter work was impeded by frequent and heavy snow falls. This may all have been acceptable if life at the base had been more pleasant. Some problems were an unavoidable result of national differences: Holtham once sat on a chair which promptly

174

collapsed under him. It was not intended to bear his 200 pounds weight. Others showed a meanness of spirit: a decree from the company forbade field officers from ordering 'luxuries', a term which seemed to apply to all the stores ordered in Kobe. There was also a decree forbidding Westerners from using firearms, which did not stop them shooting game birds. On one occasion a young boy was hit by a stray shot and there was an uproar against the assassins. The accusation of murder was somewhat damaged by the presence of the victim vociferously demanding damage. Most irritating of all were the spies sent by the government to report on the 'private conduct and personal failings of the foreign staff'. One engineer had to face the ludicrous charge of selling braces to the local people.

Holtham managed to keep his mind on the main task of railway building in difficult country. The River Toda ran in summer down a channel 400 feet wide, but when swollen by the melting snows of spring opened out to flood banks 3000 feet apart. Floods were a constant preoccupation. In 1878 water roared over the tracks at Kawasaki and Holtham turned up in person, stripping off his coat to direct the workers who were feverishly pouring ballast under the sleepers. And when he could not see what was needed, he plunged his arms into the swirling waters to feel for the gaps to plug. This did not enhance his reputation in Japanese eyes. The local engineers wore white cotton gloves which were never, under any circumstances, to be so much as spotted with dirt. Holtham's status was thus deeply compromised.

Other engineers faced equally difficult problems. William Furniss Potter surveyed the line around Lake Biwa and soon discovered that steamboat travel had its own peculiar dangers: the engineers were in the habit of tying down the safety valve on the grounds that otherwise steam would escape! His main job was supervising bridge building. He was not impressed by local building techniques:

Brickwork is little used by the Japanese and their masonry is inferior, owing to the absence of bond. This is probably caused by their system of quarrying stone, which is to split

175

large round boulders into two pieces, the result being a stone shaped like half a walnut. Of course, the large face is put on the outside of the work, and the inside is filled up anyhow, without bonding stones. As might be expected, their masonry works, such as piers and retaining walls, are not durable, though when first completed they look neat, and have the appearance of great strength.

Girder bridges were built using standardized sections sent out from Britain. As in India, the foundations were created by sinking wells. The girders, 100 feet long, were riveted together as much as 6 miles away from the site. They were then brought in by truck and laid on a temporary staging of sleepers from where they could be jacked into place. Potter reckoned to be able to complete his bridges at the rate of one girder per day. Japanese rivers, in any case, presented their own unique difficulties which Potter had to overcome.

It is a curious feature of the rivers that their beds are nearly all higher than the land through, or rather over, which they pass. The inhabitants have constructed banks to confine the water and prevent its overflowing the country: and as the beds of the rivers are gradually silted up, these banks have to be raised, so that they not unfrequently become formidable works, requiring constant care and watching to prevent their bursting. Such a catastrophe is not uncommon, and is attended sometimes with disastrous results to life and property. As the levels of the rivers vary from a few feet to 40 feet or more above the surrounding country, it is frequently a question for anxious consideration whether it is better to bridge over or tunnel under them. It will readily be seen that the country intervening between the rivers is liable, if any of the banks give way, to serious floods. On the Osako–Kioto line, especially near Kioto, this was notably the case; but it was thought desirable in this instance to keep the formation level of the railway at such a height above the ground as to be above all possible floods. This entailed lofty embankments and numerous flood openings, and greatly increased the cost of the line.

Not that cost was easy to assess.

It is impossible to give any reliable information as to the cost of the railways already constructed in Japan, owing to the system adopted by the Government of not allowing foreign engineers to interfere in, or have any control over, money matters. On each engineer's district a large staff of Japanese officials was appointed, who made all payments and arranged all contracts. Whenever an engineer required materials or labour, he had to indent on these officials, who furnished them without giving information as to cost. This system is open to many and grave objections.

Potter was only able to complete a fraction of the work he had hoped – and – expected to do. He did, however, manage to see one length of line completed and to witness the opening ceremony carried out by the Mikado. It presented an example of Japanese ingenuity. The stations 'were all beautifully decorated with evergreens, flowers and flags' and 'A huge and ugly set of sheer legs at Koha was covered with tarpaulins, fastened together and painted so as to represent their favourite mountain, Fusiyama [sic].'

There were many areas where Japanese and British worked together amicably. The Japanese soon showed that there were certain things with which they needed very little outside help, including tunnelling. But even here there were occasions when expertise was required. The 4436-foot Yanagaseyama tunnel posed ventilation problems which Holtham solved by using a turbine and compressor. The drawings were by Japanese draughtsmen working under the supervision of B.F. Wright and machine parts were cast and forged at Koha. Wright's comments on the work sum up much of the experience of the British engineers in Japan:

177

It is not the author's intention to claim anything original or novel in the design of the turbine or compressor, but to record the fact that the whole work has been made and erected by, and is now in entire charge of, men who eleven years ago had not seen a railway or machinery used for making them.

By the 1880s there was clearly a mood of growing confidence in Japan. They were prepared to tackle the Usui Pass that linked Yokogawa to Karuizawa on the Tokyo to Naortsu line. In five miles the line had to climb from Yokogawa to the Maruizawa summit, climbing a total height of 1830 feet. Various notions were considered, including loops of the Darjeeling type, but eventually the engineers settled for the Abt system, using rack and pinion pioneered in Germany. Three British engineers were involved: Francis Trevithick, C.A.W. Pownall and John McDonald. What made the line so special is that none of these engineers had tried the system before – Britain's first Abt system railway up Snowdon opened in 1896, three years after the Usui Pass. Japan was no longer blindly following British lead: she was taking the lead instead.

China was slower than Japan to take to the railway age, and no country could have had a more bizarre beginning. Gabriel James Morrison described the events of those days, beginning with a hand-written note of 1879:

The time may however come when railways will be introduced into China and I doubt not that some antiquarian may then find it interesting to make a search in the library of the Institution of Civil Engineers and to proclaim the fact that once upon a time there was a railway in China which existed over a year and on which over 40,000 train miles were run and nearly 200,000 tickets were issued.

The story began as far back as 1863 when foreign merchants in Shanghai started agitating for a railway. Then a very specific

178

proposal was brought forward for a line to connect Shanghai to the Yangtse at Woosung, and a company was set up that bought a strip of land for 'a roadway'. In 1874, two of the company set out for England to look for a contractor and came back with the news that Alexander Matheson would undertake the work and a new organization, the Woosung Road Company Ltd., now appeared. An engineer looked over the land, but still nothing was done. The proposed 'roadway' went through paddy fields and, to protect their investment, the shareholders in China ordered an embankment to be built that was capable of taking not a roadway but a railway. Mr Hill, who was put in charge of the work, was attacked by the local people and severely injured. The English investors were understandably worried, but they were assured that the Chinese authorities had given guarantees that the embankment was officially authorized and anyone interfering with the work would be punished. A narrow gauge locomotive was ordered from Rapier of Suffolk and John Dixon of London came out to lay the 2ft. 6 inch gauge track. In February 1876 a ballast train set off pulled by the engine *Pioneer* and China had its first steam train.

Early work on this railway was permitted because the local magistrate favoured Western-style development; his replacement, Feng, took precisely the opposite view. All kinds of obstacles were placed in the way of the builders, but on 1 July 1876, 4½ miles of track were opened to a temporary station at Shanghai. One hundred and fifty passengers were pulled by the loco *Celestial Empire*, but it was not a happy occasion and the station-master at Kangwa had to be evacuated on the return train. There were disputes over fencing off the line and the Chinese argued that if this was indeed a roadway anyone could use it. The inevitable happened and a man was run over and killed. Even more arguments followed before it was decided that the line was illegal, but the Company could run it anyway until the end of the year. The tracks were advanced to Woosung and on 1 January 1877 it passed to the Chinese who pulled it all up. The railway adventure was over. Morrison wrote bitterly,

179

There are apologists who will say that the Country belonged to the Chinese and they had a right to do what they liked. Those who argue in this way may have some idea of the comparatively mild opposition offered in civilised countries by a certain class, to so called innovations, but they can have no experience of dealing with a set of shrewd, cunning, conceited, and, unfortunately, powerful men, who wallow in their ignorance, and glory in the fact that they have not advanced as such for what geologists might call aeons of ages.

Other Chinese officials could take a radically different view. While the Viceroy of Nankin was ordering the demolition of the first railway, the Viceroy of the Northern Provinces, Li Hung Chang, was busy looking for ways to supply coal to the China Merchants Steam Navigation Company. The first proposal was for a 27-mile railway from the collieries to the nearest navigable river, but local authorities demanded an eighteenth-century solution: canal and tramway. Claude William Kinder was to be the engineer for the 7-mile tramway, along which it was agreed no locomotives should pass. Even with that proviso he had an extremely difficult time.

To give an idea of the annoyances practised, the following may prove interesting. While surveying, a pole was planted on the summit of a hill where the remains of a rude fortification still exist; this was reported to the throne, and several official despatches were required before the authorities were satisfied that no serious rebellion was contemplated, or the Tongsan Earth-dragon likely to be disturbed. Again, when it was proposed, some years later, to use certain iron ores to the N.E., the whole scheme was stopped as being detrimental to the manes of the imperial dead situated about 120 miles in a totally different direction, and so great was the uproar, that the colliery itself, then in full operation, was very nearly closed. The mere sight of a few boring-rods, steam-pipes, or anything with a hole in it, drove the natives frantic with fear of rebels, and for years after they persisted in the belief that, when the time was ripe, the make-belief gas- and water-pipes would become cannon or other terrible weapons of warfare. Pamphlets were circulated accusing the engineers of attempts to unearth the treasure guarded by the dragon, and calling for the immediate destruction of the works. Strikes were common, and caused much delay, to obviate which men from other provinces were imported; but, with the exception of those from Shantung and Canton, few have remained. In spite of the constant assertion that labour was abundant, it was often impossible to secure sufficient hands, especially in the summer months when they were most needed.

As on the Shanghai railway, there was a good deal of subterfuge. The line passed over very easy ground and the tramway was duly opened in 1881. But during the winter of 1880–1, secret work was going forward. An odd assortment of objects was taken to the company workshops: a boiler from an old portable engine, wheels from a scrap yard and other chunks of iron. On 9 June 1881, the engine emerged in all its glory, and was duly christened *Rocket of China*. It was the 100th anniversary of the birth of George Stephenson. There was the predictable outcry, but when the officials were given a run at 20 m.p.h. on a train headed by a Chinese locomotive built in Chinese workshops they were quite won over. The stables built for the mules were demolished, and two more engines were ordered from Robert Stephenson of Newcastle.

It was a gamble that paid off, but no one was prepared to risk another, so nothing more happened for a number of years until agreement was given for the line to be extended. Kinder was again involved, but this time work was put out to tender, and as a result it became more of an international affair: rails from Krupps of Essen, locomotives from America and a largely Chinese team. Kinder's assistant, Kwang King Yang, had been trained in America. The new encouragement for rail construction

181

was largely politically inspired, to meet what was seen as the growing power of Japan, already well set on the road to industrial power. More extensions were ordered, chiefly for military uses, but this time going all the way to Tientsin, a distance of fifty miles. The fact that this was very much an officially approved line did little to reduce local antagonisms. On the whole, however, work went well. Kinder, who built a number of lines in China did, however, find a few minor irritations.

The Chinese are excellent at all kinds of earthworks, provided sufficient care is taken to keep them in proper line and level, of which little details they are apt to be somewhat careless. The centre line was marked with pegs, 100 feet apart, duly numbered in English and Chinese, but the European figures excited official wrath, and were removed, and what was worse, in many cases the pegs themselves were taken away. In the most difficult places soldiers were employed, and their work was excellent, as they are accustomed to the construction of the mud forts so generally used in China.

Construction costs varied enormously, depending mainly on conditions. Payment was by piece rate: in the worst places, like the Petang area where men worked up to their knees in mud, they were paid 5½d. a cubic yard; in good spots it could be as low as 2d.

The earth was carried up by one man with two baskets or by two men with one large basket, the cost depending largely on the class of labour employed, *i.e.*, soldiers, canal diggers, or mere villagers and loafers. The best coolies usually do as much as 6 cubic yards a day on short leads, taking it in turns to dig and carry.

China had its own difficulties for engineers. Surveys had to be conducted in a semi-clandestine manner, without using the usual chains. Drawing attention to oneself was 'a dangerous affair in

China', and no engineer if he was wise ever went anywhere even remotely near a grave. Compromises were made all the time and, as is so often the case with compromises, rarely produced the right result. Kinder discovered that

> The Chinese, as a rule, invariably desire to have the railway
> as far from their towns, &c., as possible; but when the line
> is open, like people elsewhere, they lament that their demand
> was agreed to and acted upon.

The Europeans needed to add tact and patience to their professional skills.

Most of the problems could be traced back to the instability of a country where the old dynastic forces were weakening and there was a constant battle between the progressives and the reactionaries, between national government and provincial government, and all around were the other powers – Europe, America, Russia and increasingly Japan – looking for opportunities to cash in, hunting out trading concessions. In these circumstances the British saw railway construction as a way of infiltrating the closed world of Chinese affairs. In 1898, the British bankers Jardine Matheson joined forces with the Hong Kong and Shanghai Banking Corporation to create the British and Chinese Corporation. British interests were to lend nearly £19 million for Chinese railway building between 1894 and 1912, more than the other main financiers, France, Belgium, Germany and Japan, combined. They were not, however, any longer very active in actual construction – certainly not as active as they wished to be.

One line at least had heavy British involvement. In 1887 the Chinese authorities ordered Liu Ming Ch'uan, the governor of Formosa, to move the island's capital from the coast to the centre of the island. Liu agreed, with the premise that he would need a railway to join his new city to the port. Imperial approval was given with the proviso that foreign interference was kept to a minimum. As a result engineers, mainly British, were brought in, but were liable to be overruled by Chinese ranging from army officers to the governor himself. It was a recipe for chaos and chaos duly ensued.

The first few miles were laid out by a German engineer, but in 1888 Henry Cripps Matheson arrived from England to take over the role of consulting engineer. Most of the workforce were soldiers with no experience of railway work. Matheson would have a line pegged out only to find the next day that his soldier-navvies had taken the pegs away for firewood. Complaints had no effect: he was a foreigner. The first few miles lay through paddy fields and his attempts to take a sensible line were constantly thwarted by the officers who kept agreeing with local owners that the line should go round the edge rather than through their fields. The result was a railway that resembled an English country lane, and for much the same reason. More seriously, Matheson's engineering judgement was challenged. At Kotongka there was a difficult hilly section, but the governor refused to allow either a tunnel or a diversion. He insisted on a 60-foot-deep cutting, and ordered the military to get on with it. They, in turn, insisted on saving costs by making the cutting as narrow as possible. The result was that as fast as it was cut, the clay slid back and refilled it. The soldiers got sick and local labour was recruited, but after two years no real progress had been made.

At last the cutting was abandoned, and the tunnel approved. To save face, the authorities demanded that the actual work be done by the military; Matheson and his men were limited to setting out the line and marking depths of shafts along the way. It was a fiasco. The officers took no account of drainage problems, so that at the first major downpour the cuttings filled with landslips. They worked inwards from either end, but one entrance turned out to be 14 feet higher than the other. At this point, Matheson and the British engineers simply gave up on the whole project and went home. The only surprise is that they stayed so long. Similar problems were found by other engineers. Thomas Johnstone Bourne was resident engineer on a railway in the Lu-Pao district. Like Matheson he had problems with pegs and had to create a new position, official Peg Watchman. He was at least spared military intervention: his survey team consisted of the engineer, a European assistant, three Chinese students and a number of coolies. When work began, the contractor looked after the great army of workers, who lived in huts made of straw mats stretched over bamboo hoops. Equipment was basic: each man had one shovel and a pair of baskets on a long pole. They worked well, but other difficulties arose. The Chinese had recently established a steelworks near Hankow and insisted on supplying the rails from there. Unfortunately they appear not to have grasped the need for standardization, and the engineer was constantly being presented with a batch of rails all of different heights which it was quite impossible to fit together. In the event 30 miles of track were laid using rails imported from Britain.

In pointing up Chinese mistakes, it is as well to remember that one is reading an account written from one point of view. China was trying to leap into the modern world – moving in one bound from a feudal to an industrial society. There was national pride at stake, and that pride was easily injured by European arrogance. Chang Chih-Kung, the Chinese railway director, entered into negotiations with J.O.P. Bland of the British and Chinese Corporation over finance for the Peking to Hankow Railway. The talks soon foundered, and Chang put the Chinese case:

First he [Bland] wanted to place the construction on a contract basis, aiming at monopolising the construction rights; then he wanted the chief engineer to sign for all expenditures, aiming at interfering with China's authority in appointment and purchase. His demands were so improper that they were really beyond the realm of reason.

The problems of working in China were immense, but as the nineteenth century gave way to the twentieth the need for railway building in much of the rest of the world was dwindling, and there was no shortage of entrepreneurs looking for work. Among them was one of the most colourful characters in railway history, George Pauling. He opened offices in Hong Kong and Shanghai, but his early attempts to land contracts fell foul of politics:

attempts to run lines into Manchuria were blocked by objections from Russia and Japan. As a result, Pauling gave up on China and went off to build a railway in Borneo instead. His adventures there sound as though they were written for *Boy's Own Paper*.

He arrived in Borneo to be greeted by the agent and the news that rebellion had broken out among the Dayak head-hunters. They set off on the survey with a contingent of Sikh soldiers. That night there was an alarm, and the Sikhs began firing into the dark. Bullets whistled everywhere – up in the air, into trees, even straight through the engineers' tents. Next morning the Sikhs were sent marching back to base – facing head-hunters seemed less of a risk. In fact, shortly after the Sikhs had gone a Dayak informed them that the rebellion was over, and proved his point by unwrapping a cloth and proudly displaying the head of the chief rebel. If Dayaks proved not to be a problem, the labour-force was. The Chinese coolies were in poor health, largely because they were badly underpaid and poorly fed. Pauling called in the sub-contractor and suggested they should increase the pay. The sub-contractor decided that Pauling was mad and left the meeting bewildered at such a bizarre suggestion. But if the locals refused to listen to the Europeans, the Europeans were equally reluctant to listen to the locals. One of the surveyors, Inerny, wanted a large tree chopped down so that he could get a sighting, but the men pointed out that there was a huge bees' nest in the branches. Inerny however insisted. The axemen did their work and fled leaving Inerny sighting down his theodolite. Not for long. The irate bees descended and the surveyor had to leap into a swamp to avoid being stung to death. Unhappily the swamp was full of leeches who greeted this unexpected meal with great enthusiasm. Pauling found the story 'very amusing'. Inerny, who nearly bled to death, failed to see the joke.

Pauling's excursion into Asia was not a great success. He was soon back at the site of his real triumphs, Africa.

CHAPTER SIX

Africa

When railway building began there were, in effect, three Africas. To the north were the mainly Arab lands, with a centuries' old history of intercourse with Europe; to the far south was what had become colonial Africa, slowly but steadily spreading out from the Cape. In between was 'the dark continent', an area largely unknown and unexplored as far as Europeans were concerned. The railway histories of the three regions were as different as the regions themselves, though they did have one thing in common: every single line, at least up to the beginning of the First World War, was built to further European interests, either directly or in the role of colonial power.

The key to Africa's first railway was to be found in Asia. The ever-growing trade between Britain and India was hampered by poor communications. Ships either took the long sea route round the southern tip of Africa, or dumped off passengers and goods at Alexandria, to be taken overland to Suez, where they could continue their journey down the Red Sea. The P & O Company had their very own overland service, with some 3000 camels for freight and decidedly rough horse-drawn carriages for passengers. These jolted their hot, steamy and bumpy way to Cairo and on again to the sea. Passenger delays were acceptable to those who did not have to travel the desert roads; freight delays could be allowed; but for many a far more serious matter was the length of time the Indian mail took. Officials in India still looked to London for advice and for ratification of important decisions,

187

and it could be months between a letter being sent and an answer being received. Something clearly had to be done. The ultimate answer was the Suez Canal, but that was not yet even a dream, let alone a plan: the immediate, and obvious, answer was a railway. In 1851, the Khedive, Abbas I, gave permission for a line from Alexandria to Cairo, and Robert Stephenson was appointed chief engineer.

The theory behind railway building in Egypt was very little different from that of building the pyramids: employ enough workers and the job will be done. In this case 24,000 were employed to lay down sleepers, haul out rails and hammer home spikes. There was, however, a need for two major bridges, one over the Nile at Kafr-el-Zayat and the other over the Karrineen Canal at Birket-el-Saba. Once again, as he was to do in Canada, Stephenson opted for a tubular bridge. This time, however, there were to be differences. Both bridges crossed navigable waterways at a low level, so they had to be supplied with swinging mid-sections, and here the trains ran on top, not inside the tubes. The bridge parts were prefabricated in Britain under the supervision of Robert's cousin, George Robert Stephenson. The Nile crossing proved the more troublesome, and until it was completed, passengers had to be ferried over the river. At first, this was done in a conventional way, but soon a specially built vessel was introduced with rails on the deck, so that trains could roll on at one bank and continue their journey on the other side – a genuine train ferry. The journey across the Nile took a modest six minutes. By 1856, however, the bridge was open and the ferry retired. The line was dignified by grand termini. A correspondent writing to the *Illustrated London News* described Edwin C. Barnes' station at Alexandria as 'the most substantially constructed edifice in that city, partaking more of a European or Anglican character than most civil structures in Alexandria.' Cairo Central was more magnificent, but a good deal less Anglican, with minaret-like towers and Moorish arches. Between 1857 and 1858, the route was extended by the 'Desert line' to Suez. It enjoyed a brief prosperity until the Suez Canal was opened in 1869, when trade withered and died and the track was lifted – to be replaced in 1934.

It was 1874 before any lines were continued south of Cairo, but at much the same time work got under way along the Nile Valley even further south in the Sudan. The Nile itself remained the great route of commerce, but as navigation was brought to a halt at the cataracts, it was decided to bypass them by a 35-mile railway from Wadi Halfa. The chief engineer was John Fowler and a surveying party was marshalled on a grand scale: eight English engineers with doctor, four Egyptian engineers, a substantial army unit of officers and men, together with a train of some 400 camels accompanied by over 100 drivers and guides. When the survey was complete in 1876, work could begin, but first there was to be an impressive inauguration ceremony. Normally the route ahead would have been indicated by posts, perhaps flying flags for the ceremony. Here, however, soldiers standing rigidly to attention took the place of flag poles. It must have been exceedingly uncomfortable for them since there was a sandstorm blowing at the time. Out of the whirling clouds of the storm came the local dignitary, or Cadi, with his entourage and he at once began a lengthy address which was followed by an interminable poem. Long before it reached an end, the governor, Chatsim Pasha, indicated that enough was enough, the congregation said a devout 'amen' and the ceremony was over. The line was eventually extended to a total length of 60 miles, and then the money ran out.

The railway was not destined to have a long career. Sudan had been invaded by Turkey in 1820, and had continued under joint Turkish-Egyptian rule until Britain invaded Egypt in 1882, acting largely in the interests of the creditors of the Suez Canal Company who had not been paid by the bankrupt government. They acquired Sudan in the process, but already the Mahdi had declared a holy war against the European interlopers which culminated in the famous siege of Khartoum and the death of Gordon. The relief force retreated and Khalif Abdullah who succeeded the Mahdi ordered the railway to be destroyed.

The early lines in North Africa could hardly be called a triumph, although that was certainly not the engineers' fault. There were, however, some other minor works. Peto and Betts, for example, were contractors for the short line from Algiers to Blida. Edward Pickering promoted a couple of suburban routes around Tunis – a mere 20 kilometres of track all told – but they certainly had a very British flavour. John Chester Craven of the London, Brighton and South Coast Railway came over as chief engineer with his son William as assistant and when the system opened in 1874, the line was worked by 2–4–0T engines by Sharp Stewart. It lasted just two years before being sold off to the Italians. By then, in any case, the emphasis on rail building had moved to the opposite end of the continent.

European settlement in Southern Africa developed largely as a byproduct of the lucrative trade with the Far East. The Dutch East India Company encouraged a moderate amount of colonization, mainly so that the settlers could produce food for provisioning the Company's ships. In 1795 William V of the Netherlands fled the revolutionary armies of France to find sanctuary in England and passed over Cape Colony to Britain for 'temporary protection'. The Cape colonists had no wish to be ceded to anyone, but there were too few to resist great power manoeuvring. There were then 15,000 white settlers, mostly Dutch but with a proportion of French Huguenot refugees, and 17,000 slaves which the British were to free. It was a small colony, but one hungry for land. It was estimated that each cattle-raising family needed at least 6000 acres to feed their stock. There was not, however, any great pressure to extend colonization at this stage. The British were simply not interested: other regions, notably India, offered far richer pickings. The Cape Colony developed so slowly that there was no obvious need to rush into railway building.

The first attempt to get construction in South Africa under way began, predictably perhaps, in England at the height of the railway mania. The Cape of Good Hope Western Railway held its first meeting in London in 1845. It had apparently impeccable credentials. The legal adviser was named as William Porter, the Attorney General of the Cape Colony, but unfortunately nobody had asked him if he wished to act in this capacity. He did not, and went on to describe the whole scheme as 'hopeless'. No more was heard of it. There was a pause until another company was registered in London, the Cape Town Railway and Dock Company with a registered capital of £600,000 and more importantly a guarantee of interest payments by the government. Sir Charles Fox was appointed chief engineer but as in other cases had little to do with the project himself and sent over one of his assistants, William George Brounger, to be the man on the spot. Brounger was, in fact, destined to stay on for a successful engineering career in South Africa. On 1 March 1859, the first sod was cut before what was, for the region, a massive crowd of around 6000. It was 1863 before the line reached Wellington, but already in 1859 the first locomotive had been delivered from Hawthorn's, an 0–4–2T which came complete with its own engineer-fitter-driver, William Dabbs. It was curiously numbered No. 9; 1 to 8 were destined never to appear. Dabbs having built the engine obviously became attached to it, for he remained as driver of No. 9 throughout his working life. Locomotive No. 9 was not the only arrival from Britain, a navvy gang also came to work on the line, and proceeded to live up to their reputation, with a riot at Salt River. Nonetheless several of the navvies, like Driver Dabbs, stayed on in the country. The line was intended from the first to encourage settlement, and anyone building a house worth at least £70 within a mile of any of the new stations was given free tickets for eight years.

Other small lines were built at much the same time. Brounger built a branch line to the Cape Town suburb of Wynberg, chiefly notable for one of its unusual rules. One thinks of anti-smoking campaigns as being very much a late twentieth-century phenomenon, but on this line anyone choosing to use one of the second-class smoking cars had to pay the full first-class fare. A second system was begun in Natal in 1860, on the opposite coast from Cape Town – a 2-mile route from Durban to the Customs House at Durban Point.

By 1875, a mere 155 miles had been completed in the whole region, but it was quite clear that more were going to be needed, and rather belatedly the question of gauge was considered. Up to then the main lines had been 'standard' 4 ft. 8½ ins, but the government decided, wisely, given the fact that railways would be penetrating ever more difficult country, to settle on a new standard of 3 ft. 6 ins. There began a period of rapid rail expansion, given a great fillip by the opening up of the diamond mines at Kimberley. They were rumbustious times in Southern Africa. In 1887 the Netherlands South African Railway decided to build a line through to the east-coast port of Lourenco Marques in the Portuguese colony of Mozambique. Work began under an American contractor, Edward McMurdo, but he soon sold out to the Delgao Bay and East African Railway Company of London. Sir Thomas Tancred was appointed chief engineer. The major part of the workforce consisted of around 3000 African labourers, but the old habit persisted of 'stiffening' the local force with a backbone of tried and true British navvies. Many of the batch who came over turned out to have been 'tried' in a different sense, in the courts rather than on the diggings. There was a hard core of mainly army deserters who came to be known as 'The Irish Brigade' and they terrorized whoever they settled amongst. At Lourenco Marques they took offence at the Portuguese authorities' attempts to discipline them, and sent a note signed 'Captain Moonlight' announcing that they would wreck the fort and the Portuguese gun boat in the harbour. The police followed a group of the navvies back to their hotel where the sounds of revelry suggested that a great party was going on. The police waited until peace descended then crept up to arrest the surviving drunks – and found there was only half a dozen there, whooping it up as decoys. In the meantime the fort and gunboat had been duly wrecked as threatened. Working out in the Transvaal they managed virtually to destroy an entire township. They did, however, do their job, and do it well under appalling conditions, pushing the lines on through mosquito-infested malarial swamps. When the lines reached the border, a great celebration was planned and dignitaries waited for the train full of food and wine to arrive. It arrived late, empty apart from a brief note informing the guests that the food was excellent and assuring the chief engineer that his health was being copiously drunk. It was signed, of course, by the Irish Brigade.

In such a country, and under such conditions, it needed a man of particular qualities to hold the whole system together and make it work. One such man was the contractor George Pauling, already mentioned for his work in Borneo. He was a man largely forced to make his own way in the world, mostly thanks to an improvident father. In about 1870 he managed to get work with Ralph Firbank, whose uncle Joseph Firbank was an important railway contractor. Pauling was soon gaining valuable experience as a time-keeper on the Wood Green to Enfield railway, but it all ended when his father did one of his none too infrequent disappearing acts, with numerous creditors in close but unavailing pursuit. The young Pauling went on to get what work he could, which included a spell on the notoriously difficult Settle and Carlisle line, excellent training for his later life. In 1874 his father was given an engineering appointment on the Cape Government Railway and young George followed to seek his fortune. He was sent to work on the Grahamstown line in the Eastern Province, but very quickly realized that the world was full of competent engineers, but desperately short of able contractors. He leaped boldly in, quite undeterred by the fact that he had no experience as a contractor and not one penny of capital. He went into partnership with an English foreman, Billy Frith, for work on a tunnel, and financed the enterprise by setting up a store at the tunnel end to sell goods to the work force – a splendid system as far as Pauling was concerned and one by which the workers subsidized their own wages. He tried for more contracts, but the company were, not unreasonably, unconvinced of his ability to manage a major undertaking. Pauling was undeterred and tendered again using an unlikely front – a consortium consisting of an Italian, a Scot and an old English navvy. It worked up to a point, but Pauling had not allowed for the astonishing ability of the navvy to spend cash, regardless of commitments. He 'developed an unfortunate habit of remaining in Grahamstown and disposing of it in riotous living.' On one occasion Pauling tracked him down to a brothel where he had been fleeced out of £400 which was only retrieved with a good deal of difficulty. At the same time, one cannot help feeling that Pauling had found a kindred spirit. His own verdict on the navvy partner was far from unkind:

With all his faults he was an affectionate old chap and really very fond of me. He was incapable of bearing malice, and during the intermittent periods when he was sober he invariably acknowledged that I was his best friend.

Pauling's work schedule was exacting.

By four o'clock in the morning I was generally out of bed and away on horseback to inspect the work that was in progress beyond Ross's camp. I then visited practically every bit of work that was being carried on and was back at my camp at Wadi Nek tunnel before breakfast. After a bath and a morning meal I supervised my own work in the tunnel until the middle of the day. Then a snack and on horse again to ride right through the work and back to my camp. But I was not indifferent to the enjoyment of ordinary pleasures and, considering myself entitled to a little recreation, it was my habit to go into Grahamstown to the Masonic Hall, enjoy a good dinner, drink freely with congenial spirits, and play billiards till the hotel closed. Riding back to camp I usually arrived there before midnight.

What he does not mention in that account was the party trick he would perform at the Masonic Hall. This was to pick up his pony, weighing around 450 pounds, and carry it on his shoulders right round the billiard room. One night he overreached himself, and wagered he could carry the pony upstairs. He failed and toppled down with the pony on top of him. Pauling was alright, but the pony refused to co-operate in any more shenanigans. He was, in every sense, larger than life, with gargantuan appetites to match his physique. He recorded how, on one occasion, he and two companions breakfasted on eight bottles of champagne and a thousand oysters. He did, however, add modestly that 'the oysters were small.' His friends matched him for zest and extravagance. One of them, 'Old Dr Williams', succumbed to one of the many brands of fever that raged in tropical Africa. Pauling and the rest began to lay bets on how long he would live. The old man lay there, soaked in perspiration and at last opened one eye and crooked a finger. Pauling leaned over to catch his words: 'Bet another £10 for me.' Naturally, with such a large sum resting on the issue, he recovered. Pauling was prepared to accept any challenge and travel anywhere in the world to build a railway. This was the man who was to be for Africa what Brassey and Peto had been for Britain and so many other parts of the world.

He soon showed that he had an eye for the main chance. Whilst working at Grahamstown, he hit on a railway scheme of his own. Grahamstown itself was linked to the sea by a 110-mile river trip to Port Elizabeth. A far shorter route was available overland to Port Alfred. Pauling proposed to the government that if they would agree to subsidize the line, he would undertake to raise the rest of the capital in England. The government agreed to put up £1500 a mile and Pauling set off, armed with a photograph showing the harbour at Port Alfred crowded with craft. What the photograph did not have was any indication of scale: the English investors were not to know that most of the 'cargo vessels' shown in the picture were scarcely bigger than rowing boats on the Serpentine. In the meantime, Pauling went back to his old mentor, Ralph Firbank, and formed Firbank and Pauling. The scheme was not quite the get-rich-quick affair that Pauling had planned: the government were cannier than he thought and held back until the job was complete. His troubles were compounded when Ralph Firbank died unexpectedly, but Pauling was nothing if not resourceful. He had other irons in the fire. Roller skating had just become a craze, and work on the railway to Port Alfred was, for a time, subsidized by profits from the Pauling skating rink – to be recouped when the final government payments were made. This remained typical of the man throughout his life: if one speculation failed, then, no problem, there was always another ready to hop into its place.

Pauling was, not surprisingly, frequently at odds with authority. Government engineers preferred day work to contract work, so that their income depended on time spent on a job, while the contractors' rate was fixed. They insisted on absurd conditions. Station platforms were extended far beyond the length of any train that was ever to use them; stone work for even an insignificant bridge over a dried up water course had to be of a standard that would fit a palace or cathedral. Pauling held out for reasonable economy, and as a result the government inspector issued an edict that no one was to speak to him. It was not a wise decision. Pauling met the man as he was leaving his house.

> Mad with rage, I went up to him, and after a few brief but incisive words I knocked him down. He refused to get up. I gave him one or two gentle kicks, just to help him up, when his wife appeared on the scene. I was so enraged that I picked him up off the ground and, although he weighed over twelve stones, I threw him against his wife and both of them fell into the doorway of the cottage.

He then marched across to the engineering staff and told them, 'succinctly if profanely', precisely what he thought of them.

South Africa was a troubled region in the 1880s. There had been wars against the Zulus, fought with singular incompetence by the British, and this had been one of the factors that had led the Boers to seek independence from British rule. The Transvaal and the Orange Free State were given a degree of independence, under British suzerainty. There was little love lost between British and Boer. In the normal way of things no Briton could have expected to be awarded a contract in these areas: Pauling was the exception. Some years before, the Boer leader Paul Kruger had arrived at the town of Krankuil where the English-speaking hotelier had refused Kruger and his associates a room. Overhearing the argument, Pauling's brother Harry had offered them the hospitality of the work camp, not luxurious but with beds, food and, no doubt, a good deal of drink. Kruger did not forget, and Pauling had the pick of the contracts. Some he may have regretted taking, especially the line to Crocodile Point, a wretched spot where fever raged. One of Pauling's remedies for low morale was to run a nightly lottery on who would have the highest temperature: the winner was frequently too delirious to be aware of his victory.

Pauling stories soon multiplied. A gentleman with the grand name of John Percy FitzPatrick appeared, claiming to have the concession for supplying all goods and provisions for the workforce but providing no written authority. Pauling waited until FitzPatrick had built his store, fitted it out and filled the shelves before sending a note saying that unfortunately Mr FitzPatrick's new store was on the site selected for a quarry. Blasting, Pauling said, would start shortly. Store and goods disappeared more quickly than they arrived. Again, it was typical of Pauling to hold a sports day at Christmas, when the thermometer read 115°F. He does not, alas, recall how many volunteered for the races. It was on this line to Crocodile Point that the workforce gave him his nickname, The Great Crocodile, beating the fictional Mr Dundee by a century.

Divisions between English-speaking settlers and the Boers deepened in the 1880s and 1890s. A huge expanse to the north of the Cape states, almost half a million square miles, was given by Royal Charter to Cecil Rhodes' British South Africa Company, and was to become known as Rhodesia. It was largely unexplored and unsettled, and it was soon clear that the key to future success lay in establishing transport routes with the rest of the world. In 1888, Sir Charles Metcalfe surveyed a line northwards from Kimberley, the furthest point on the line from the Cape system to Vryburg in what was then British Bechuanaland. It was a start, but far from satisfactory. Rhodes himself took the long trek north from the railhead to Fort Salisbury by oxcart, and one trip was enough to convince him that the future lay with railways. This view was strongly reinforced in the rainy season of 1890–1 when all wheeled transport was brought to a halt in the spreading quagmire, and several pioneering families were marooned on the open veldt. The most direct route north was difficult for it had to pass through the land of the Matabele whose chief Lobengula was firmly opposed to the European settler and notoriously warlike. An alternative had to be found and the best answer was to ignore the overland route to the Cape altogether and strike out from Salisbury and head for the port of Beira in Portuguese Mozambique. The contract for the 2 ft. gauge line went to Pauling. It was just his sort of challenge combining danger from disease and wild animals, route-finding through virtually unknown territory and a handsome profit for the man strong enough to see it through. The route led through the fetid coastal plain and wound up through the Udz mountains on its way to Salisbury. Disease was rampant, and six white men died of fever in a fortnight; there are no records of how many of those referred to by Pauling as either 'niggers' or 'kaffirs' succumbed. Supplies for the first part of the line were brought upriver from Beira in lighters hauled by two steam tugs. This worked well for a time, but when the rains came the river overflowed its banks and became one wide lake. The tug *Agnes* strayed out of the channel altogether and was caught by a sudden drop in level and was literally left high and dry, not even on the bank but seven miles from the normal river course. There it stayed for three years until another flood floated it free.

The local wildlife was regarded as a source of food and sport: Pauling's cousin shot eight buffalo one morning before breakfast. The wildlife was, however, quite capable of fighting back. Pauling records:

On one occasion, when Lawley, Mr. Moore, who was the company's engineer, and I were going back from the Muda River ballast hole to Fontesvilla, the road was in a bad condition and the engine had left the rails three or four times in a distance of a few miles. It behoved us, therefore, to travel very slowly and with extreme caution. There was one truck beyond the engine in which we three were accommodated. We were creeping along at about four miles an hour, taking no particular heed of our surroundings, when suddenly the engine driver discovered ahead a herd of lions, lionesses, and cubs, resting in the side cutting which ran alongside the railway bank. It was an awe-inspiring sight, and the driver was for a moment nonplussed. He knew that he dare not increase speed and run the risk of another derailment. There was not a gun on the train. Few men are valiant in the immediate presence of wild lions, and we three 'passengers' deemed it expedient to scramble out of the truck and on to the side of the engine away from the herd. With a view to making as much noise as possible the driver opened his whistle and cylinder cocks and commenced to creep past the place where the lions were resting. The noise was too much for them for they all bolted with the exception of one stately old lioness, who stood her ground, and snarled at us as we passed. Had we remained in the truck it is not improbable that she would have made a jump at one of us, but she funked the engine and its steam and noise. Having reached a position of security we counted in all thirty-two lions, lionesses and cubs.

Other workers on the line had even more harrowing experiences. On one occasion Pauling set out on an inspection tour on a trolley – in which he nearly bumped into a large lion. He then came to a point where there was a water tower and a small camp for the permanent way gang.

I arrived there about seven in the morning, and was surprised to find nobody about. I therefore shouted, and in response one of the white men emerged timidly from the tent. I spoke severely to him, because the man ought to have been at his work at daybreak. Then I noticed the kafirs beginning to descend from the water tank. I asked what it meant. It appeared that the noise of my trolley and the shouting of my boys had driven away two lions which had been besieging the men in the tent, and the kafirs had escaped into the tank to get out of the way. The white men showed me where one of the lions had been sweeping under the tent with one of his paws, trying to reach them. They had been dodging from one part of the tent to another to avoid the lion's claws. The marks were quite plain on the floor of the tent, so I refrained from reprimanding these men for not being at their work as early as they ought to have been under normal conditions.

While work continued on the Beira, there was a return to building in the south. Rhodes promoted an extension of the Cape line to the flyblown border town of Mafeking, a huddle of shacks and corrugated-iron stores. Its character began to change dramatically with the coming of the railways which brought speculators scurrying north, buying up land and building substantial hotels and shops. Now, in 1893, new plans were brought forward for an advance to Bulawayo, and a junction with the Beira Railway – even though there was an obvious problem up ahead where the 3 ft. 6 in. gauge line met the 2 ft. gauge. Other human difficulties were also having to be faced.

Lobengula and the Matabele were active again, engaging in their centuries' old pattern of raids on the neighbouring Mashonas. This had been the pattern for as long as anyone could remember, but now European values were being applied in the region: such behaviour was an affront to white rule. A punitive mission was sent to Bulawayo, Lobengula's capital. The leader set fire to the town and retreated. A party following under Major Alan Wilson was trapped by a flooded river and found itself the attacked not the attacker: it was annihilated. Lobengula retired beyond the Zambesi, but both the Matabele and the Mashona continued raiding each other and the settlers. To Cecil Rhodes the answer was clear: the new country he was building needed its railway and needed it fast. This point was dramatically reinforced when rinderpest wiped out a vast number of cattle in the land, bringing wheeled transport to a halt. The ox cart alone was not enough. Rhodes was to bring even more trouble on his own head with his ill-advised attack on Kruger and the Boers. He firmly believed that the Vitlanders, the English-speaking population of the Transvaal, were ready to rise up in rebellion if given the chance. He offered them the chance in the form of an armed raid led by an old crony, Dr Leander Starr Jameson. It was a fiasco: there was no general uprising and not only were the Boers infuriated, but the British government were scarcely less displeased at the prospect of a private citizen declaring unofficial war on a neighbouring state. The conditions were certainly not propitious for orderly railway construction, but Rhodes cajoled the builders to continue as fast as they could with no regard to niceties.

The Chartered Company of South Africa gave guaranteed interest on capital of £2 million and Pauling took the contract. It was 492 miles from railhead to Bulawayo: Pauling completed it in 500 working days. The instructions had been to create a line that would be 'capable of effectively conveying traffic at a speed of twelve miles an hour on completion', but that gradients and curves should be kept to normal main line standards. This meant skimping elsewhere. The line followed the flattest ground so that sleepers could wherever possible be laid with little or no ballast. Shallow gulleys, streams and even rivers were crossed without the luxury of bridges – these could be added later when time was less pressing. In some places rails actually lay just below the water surface, so that trains would edge gingerly down the bank, slide down into the water with a hissing plume of steam and pull out again up the other side. It must have made for interesting travel. It might have been even more interesting to passengers if they had known just how confident the railway company was about this particular system. Weather can change with startling rapidity in Africa, and there was always the possibility that a train having crossed one gulley would find the next one flooded and the one behind filling up rapidly. To cope with this eventuality the company arranged for a supply wagon to be attached to each train with enough food and water for the passengers for *one month*.

The opening of the line in November 1897 was a triumph, though Cecil Rhodes himself was not there to see it: the Jameson cloud still hung over his head. There was a great deal of jingoism, notably from the British representative of the House of Commons, Colonel Saunderson, whose speech was widely reported.

They had an Englishman making a railway on the Nile; they had an Englishman building a railway to Bulawayo. He would like to know what force on earth could prevent the two joining hands!

201

This dream – of a continuous route from Cape to Cairo – was to remain unrealized. The local paper was left to sound a more reasonable note.

We have not a London and North Western, or a Midland Railway to work with, but a line which is faulty in many respects owing to the rapidity with which it has been constructed. There is much to be done to it before it can be made a permanent railway. Bridges have to be built, gradients and curves altered and points rectified before the locomotive will run with the smoothness and regularity which are the pride of the English General Manager. Such a consummation could not be expected at this early date, and when the visitors take all the obstacles into consideration it will seem remarkable that the line was constructed at all through miles of country without water or food for man or beast. Water for the engines had to be dragged hundreds of miles, and when Mr. Pauling suggested the speedy completion of the railway many people thought the proposition an incredible one, on account of the country which had to be passed through. Still Pauling Bros. were as good, or rather better than their word and had the line laid before the time they specified.

But with the Bulawayo line open, Rhodes was already dreaming of new extensions and in June 1890, work began on the line to Gwelo. It had scarcely got under way before all such plans had to be abandoned at the outbreak of the Boer War. New imperatives now appeared.

Within weeks of the outbreak of war, Baden-Powell and his Rhodesian Regiment found themselves trapped in Mafeking, and the way south was closed. The gauge break on the Beira Railway at Umtali between the 2 ft. line to the coast and the 3 ft. 6 in. line to Salisbury, which had seemed a minor nuisance, now looked more like a transport disaster. Every effort had to be put into the task of improving the system within Rhodesia itself. In old comic books, characters faced by an impossible situation used to snort 'this looks like a job for Superman'; at the end of the last century in Africa, they called for George Pauling. It was Pauling and the resident engineer A.L. Lawley who marshalled the forces that went to the relief of Mafeking; and it was Pauling and Lawley who had the entire Beira to Umtali line relaid to 3 ft. 6 in. gauge. They had a workforce of 7000 men and they managed the whole job by 1 August 1900, without any disruption to the supplies running on the old narrow gauge line. In the process, they even managed to cut twelve miles off the old route.

At the end of the war, dreams of the Cape to Cairo route were revived, and plans were put forward for a very ambitious route that would run all the way up to Lake Tanganyika to link with the proposed Uganda Railway. The idea was shelved in favour of a more modest proposal, a line to the newly discovered coalfield at Wankie. This would have to cross the Zambesi, and Cecil Rhodes proposed that the engineers should make a virtue of necessity and create the world's most spectacular railway bridge, bringing passengers within sight of the great Victoria Falls. He was to die in 1902, before the work was completed. It was intended to create a rail spectacular; in the process a major engineering headache was also created. It was, at the time, the highest bridge above water in the world – 420 feet above the low water mark – and near enough to the falls for the spray to beat against the carriage windows. All that was needed was to throw a simple span of iron across this mighty rock gorge. The designer was George Andrew Hobson of Sir Douglas Fox and partners. Hobson described how the start was a little discouraging.

> The rock being very hard, the bridge was designed to fit the profile of the gorge with as little expenditure on excavation as possible; and it would have done so, but for a mistake made by the surveyor in concluding that the rock on both sides was solid. The mistake was perhaps excusable, and was not discovered until the vegetation which thrives in the hot sun and the spray from the falls had been removed, and the work of clearing the ground and the excavation of the rock had proceeded for some time. It was then found that the shelf on the right bank on which it was intended to rest one

end of the principal span was covered to a considerable
depth with debris. By the time the error had been discovered,
the preparation of the steelwork was too far advanced to per-
mit of any alteration being made in the structure. The difficulty had therefore to be overcome partly by increasing the
depth of the concrete foundations, and partly by lowering
the level of the entire bridge to the extent of 21 ft.; but both
time and money would have been saved had the true facts
of the case been recognised at the beginning, the span
designed 25 feet longer, and the truss increased in depth at
the ends by 20 ft.

Once work got under way, two parties were assembled, one on
each side of the gorge, and their first job was to establish communication by telephone. The first attempt involved attaching a
line to a kite and letting the wind carry it over. The kite was
raised, released and proceeded to dance very prettily in the eddies,
but refused to go anywhere near the opposite bank. After that
a rocket was fired across, which worked perfectly, and a marked
wire was used to check the surveyors' measurements of the width
of the gorge. This was followed by a cableway which was to be
the main transport system until the bridge itself was complete.
One of the young engineers working on site was a member of the
Fox family, C. Beresford Fox, who described the excitement of
the first gorge crossing in a letter home, dated 21 November 1903.

Well, I am crossing the gorge almost daily now by the wire
rope: it is such a saving of time and trouble; but the first
sensation is almost terrific. I was the first to cross, and did
so from the north to the south side. The cable is a ⅝-in.
diameter steel wire rope, 900 ft. in length, and is supported
at each side by a solid post 2 ft. in diameter, let down into
the rock some 7 or 8 ft. Then a ¼-in. stranded wire acts as
an endless hauling rope round a windlass at one side and a
pulley on the other.
The running pulley is, however, not quite satisfactory,
as we could not obtain a trolley in Bulawayo, and so,

temporarily, have to do the best we can; the present arrangement is safe, but not good mechanically.

As they tied me into the 'bosun's chair' I must admit to feeling a bit strange in relying absolutely on my own calculations for my safety. The chair is a piece of wood suspended by four ropes, with a canvas back and a sack and board as a foot rest. Of course one is so tied in that were you to lose consciousness you could not fall out; this precaution, for some people, is advisable.

All ready, so they gave the signal to the windlass on the south side, and I felt the endless rope tightening and pulling up the slack, and slowly out the pulley ran.

The precipice is so steep on the north side that after five yards of one's journey you are hanging over a 100-ft. depth. and after thirty yards over the rushing water 400 ft. below – more than the height of St. Paul's Cathedral. It was a novel experience and one well worth feeling, as the eye finds it so difficult to give a correct impression of the height – the stereoscopic effect is not great enough in looking downwards (a most unusual direction); but as the 'boys' working at the bridge hurled down huge boulders and stones I then noticed that the long time taken for these to reach the water below me was much more startling than when seen from the opposite side. No downward motion can be discerned, only the dwindling of the rock in size, due to the perspective effect, as it falls lower and lower before reaching the water with a report like blasting and a splash more than 50 ft. in height. I found myself quite relieved when directly over the water, with no prospect of falling on to a rock in the event of the rope breaking.

After the first few moments there is a real charm in looking down; nothing but space between you and the water, save for the 'sag' of the returning endless wire; the small trees and even the large ones on the south ledge bearing such a different appearance below.

Of course the predominant thought is, what would one feel if the pulley broke, whether you would really be

unconscious after the first 100 ft., and whether the last jerk
you felt isn't the cable snapping; and you hurriedly look
down to see if the water and rocks are not rushing up to meet
you in your downward flight, and are relieved to see the
cable still intact and stretching in a graceful curve to either
side of the gorge.

Such a comfortable sensation too, on a sagging rope – a
smooth, gliding motion, and but for the slight vibration
caused by the pulley running over the separate strands, more
like that of a boat, with a steady rise and fall, and perhaps
a slight swinging of the chair from side to side.

This journey of 300 yds. through the air saves a detour of
9 to 10 miles by land and river, and gives a good idea of the
splendid view which will be obtained from the bridge, when
completed, of the superb scenery.

The early work was also exciting in a different way.

Excavation for bridge is getting on slowly only, owing to the
impossibility of getting 'boys'; there is also such a great deal
of cleaning down of the sides of the cliff, to get rid of loose
boulders, that the work has been increased in amount. Of
course on the north side the *debris* you clear away falls into
the water below, but on this side it falls 80 ft. and then rolls,
and will mostly have to be shifted again, unavoidably too,
owing to the ledge of rock.

What erratic courses falling boulders take! You start a
large one from the top – probably it breaks, and the pieces
go in all directions within 45° of its original course; but often
the whole boulder on landing takes an entirely new route,
and goes crashing through the brushwood beyond the 60-ft.
clearing, and away over the ledge at least 100 ft. to the right
or left of where it started.

He also had more mundane matters to deal with.

I am putting up some fifteen or twenty huts for the railway
company, or for the men and boys, *e.g.* a bedroom hut (all

circular), 13 ft. or 14 ft. diameter inside, about 7 ft. or 8 ft. walls, and a sloping conical roof another 12 ft. high. It is made of poles cut out of the bush, and placed close together all round save for doors or windows. The roof is then thatched with good grass, and the walls and floors 'dargha'd', *i.e.* plastered with clay hiding the poles completely; and then you have a delightfully cool and waterproof dwelling.

The workers had a number of problems to cope with. Cecil Rhodes had the romantic notion of passengers looking at the falls through spray-lashed windows; it perhaps never occurred to him that this inevitably also meant spray-lashed construction gangs. However, the work went steadily forward, as the cantilevers were steadily advanced from either side, until the two halves of the arch met with perfect precision on 1 April 1905 – and there was no unexpected April Fool's Day disaster to mar the occasion.

While the bridge was still being built, the line was being continued northwards, at some speed, as a French engineer was to discover. He asked the chief engineer, Sir Charles Metcalfe, how much track could be laid in a day. Sir Charles in his turn asked him to make a guess, and the Frenchman came up with an estimate of half a mile. Sir Charles had a word with the assistant engineer, the engineer spoke to the foreman and the foreman spoke to the gang. A whistle was blown and work began. When a quarter of a mile of track was complete, the whistle was blown again and the stop watch consulted. Twenty minutes had passed from start to finish. It seemed unlikely that a pace like that could be kept up for long, but Sir Charles was intrigued to find out just how much track could be laid in one day. They managed 5¾ miles. Americans had recently begun using the latest automatic track-laying machines. In the same period, they could only set down four and a half.

The line pushed steadily north, held up less by engineering problems than by financial. There was a long stop at Broken Hill, but by November 1909 the line that had started at the Cape now extended all the way to the border with the Belgian Congo. Although the main line received most of the attention it was not the only route being built in the region. One line was intended as part of a system that would link the coast, not this time to Salisbury but to Lake Nyasa. The starting point was to be Port Herald on the Shire River, a tributary of the Zambesi. From here the line would head north for over a hundred miles to Blantyre, with the possibility of a later extension to the lake itself being kept in mind. It stands as a classic case of the follies that can occur when bureaucrats in London impose conditions on the engineers in the field – conditions which have everything to do with politics and nothing to do with practical solutions to practical problems.

The original plan had called for a line that would start at Chiromo, some 30 miles north of Port Herald, but the river was so treacherous with shallows and constantly shifting sandbanks that it was decided that no river craft would ever reach there – hence the extra rail mileage to Port Herald. Chiromo was, however, to be the place where the railway crossed the river on a substantial bridge, over 400 feet long. At least, the engineers felt, there was one thing on which everyone was agreed – there would be no river traffic. That was certain. They had not made allowances for the Whitehall mentality. There was certainly no chance of river traffic *now*, but what if circumstances changed. Exactly what circumstances might change to make this wholly unnavigable river usable by anything larger than a canoe was never explained. Nevertheless it was insisted that the bridge would have to be pierced with a centre span 100 feet wide, giving a head room above high water of 30 feet. It was wholly impractical to build to that height, so either a lift or swing bridge was needed. The conventional swing and drawbridge were of no use, when only manual labour was available, so ingenuity was exercised in building a new type of lift bridge. Towers were built at either side of the statutory 100 feet gap with large cogs at the top. Chains passed over the cogs with the span at one end and counterweights at the other. Mechanical force only had to overcome friction, though for a structure of that size that was bad enough. It took eight men winding the windlass for half an hour to raise the bridge. The parts were made in Britain, shipped out to Africa and erected. At this point the fickle River Shire went through one of its periodic changes of direction. Sand built up under the new span and the main channel diverted itself to go under one of the fixed spans. The whole exercise had proved entirely futile. In time even Port Herald was to be left stranded and the line had to be extended even further south to the Zambesi itself. It was 1915 before the line eventually reached the lake. The lake itself was controlled, in 1914, by the Germans who had a gunboat to make sure it stayed that way. But at the outbreak of the war, a small force came up the railway, disabled the gunboat and claimed the lake; it is generally thought of as Britain's first naval victory in the war, and was the inspiration for C.S. Forester's novel, *The African Queen*.

Lines were pushed inland in a rather tentative way from various places along the west coast of Africa at the very end of the nineteenth century. The process began in Sierra Leone with a very grandiose promotion for what was called the Grand Sahara Railway. This was one of those lines that looked very pretty when drawn on a coloured map in London but was wholly impractical to anyone with even the slightest knowledge of northern Africa. It was soon dropped. After that a more systematic approach was adopted. Sir William Shelford was approached by the Crown Agent for the Colonies and asked to conduct a survey of possible railway routes along the West African coast. He decided to begin in Sierra Leone. He had no plans to visit the region himself, but appointed the engineering company of Bradford, Knights and Hayton. W. Bradford was the man who drew the short straw for a trip to the 'fever coast'. In spite of the medical staff that was sent out and the field hospitals that were established, four of the European staff died from tropical diseases between November 1895 and April 1896. It did not seem from the map to be a very adventurous line, pushing just a few miles inland from Freetown to Songo, and even the long-term ambitions of a line to the Liberian frontier only represented a route of around 100 miles of narrow gauge, 2 ft. 6 in. track. But that made no allowance for the atrocious conditions under which the men had to work, hacking their way through dense forest, clearing tall trees simply to

209

get a line of sight. There were no maps, and no way of getting an overall view of the territory. An engineer had to rely as much as anything on experience and instinct, and even then he could never be sure that there was not a better line to be had perhaps no more than a few hundred yards away, out of sight in the deep forest.

The same conditions were true on other routes inaugurated by Shelford. The Gold Coast had an excellent case for railway construction. The name was not fanciful: gold was found, not, unfortunately for the miners, on the coast, but some forty miles inland and protected by thick jungle. The railway surveyors selected what was at the time a huddle of huts along the shore at a village called Sekondi as the harbour and terminus of the railway. The actual survey was extraordinarily difficult. The land was full of humps and hollows under a thick cover of vegetation that evened them all out as far as the eye could detect. As a result, a surveyor could walk along what appeared level ground only to plunge up to his thighs in filthy water while releasing a cloud of mosquitoes eager to welcome the arrival of a substantial meal. Unexpected difficulties arose. The teams followed the usual pattern of clearing an area through the trees for sight lines, and then marking out the route with wooden pegs. They had not allowed for the extraordinary fecundity of the jungle. The pegs cut from green wood had scarcely been stuck in the ground before they began putting out fresh shoots, and by the time the surveyors returned, their surveying pegs were indistinguishable from any other forest saplings. In spite of all these problems, a line was built, but only at a cost of great personal hardship. Between August 1898 and May 1901, no fewer than ten chief engineers were appointed, as one after the other fell sick and had to leave the region. Other railways along the coast were built; all presented great problems. In Nigeria, for example, where building out of Lagos began in 1893, the main obstacle was the river Niger, not bridged until 1916. But if any one line could be said to sum up the African experience, then it must be the Kenya and Uganda Railway. Such was its share of hardships, failure, triumphs and high drama that it was known – for reasons that became all too apparent to everyone concerned in its construction – as 'The Lunatic Line'.

The ostensible object of the railway was that noble one of laying a line to the interior that would hit at the heart of the slave trade: the actual motive was to reach Lake Victoria and establish territorial rights before the Germans. The line was the responsibility of the Imperial British East African Company, but was paid for by the British Government. In August 1891, Major J.R.L. Macdonald was appointed chief engineer. He had just returned from India where he had been engineer on one railway and had surveyed two more. An expedition had already been sent out under Captain Lugard to raise the flag in 1890, and now he was to be followed by Macdonald's survey party. Local opinion had it that in order to travel into the interior, he would need a company of native infantry and a Maxim gun. Instead he opted for a party of forty, made up of Pathans and Punjabis, who as well as being experienced chainmen and staff-holders were ferocious fighters. However, as he was being asked to conduct a survey over 500 miles of difficult country in just nine months he did request some help. Three Royal Engineer officers were added to the party to help with the work, and Captain Pringle was made second-in-command. The balance between military and civilian duties was neatly encapsulated in his own account, *Soldiering and Surveying in British East Africa*.

The route was to begin on the Kenya coast at Mombasa and Macdonald, viewing it for the first time, found it 'far from cheering from the standpoint of a railway survey, though wonderfully beautiful from an artistic standpoint.' He was also introduced to the pack animals bought for the expedition – 120 donkeys – but by the time Macdonald saw them half had already died 'and others were evidently desirous of following the bad example thus set.' Macdonald then set off with Pringle to try their hand at a little triangulation on a plateau fifteen miles from the coast. It was not an encouraging experience.

The discomforts of this preliminary canter were considerable; it rained on the average twice a day, and on one occasion my camp went astray. We laboriously cut our way through dense jungle to the summit of a commanding hill, only to find that the view did not extend to a greater distance than fifty yards. We realised the pleasures of chaining a base in long wet grass, full of holes and pools of water in which the chainmen not infrequently took an involuntary bath, a proceeding not conducive to accuracy in measurement. To add to my discomfort, my interpreter was a fraud as regards his knowledge of English, and supplemented it by a barbarous lingo which he called Hindustani, but which had little resemblance to the Hindustani spoken in India. When we got back to Mombasa after five days of this sort of thing, we both agreed that survey work in the interior could not be classed as altogether amusing!

Macdonald seems to have been a man blessed with a laconic sense of humour, and he needed it. The time had come to start the survey proper: Pringle was to take one contingent and follow the well established caravan route; Macdonald adopted the more difficult task of hunting for a wholly new line along the valley of the Sabalei River. The day of departure arrived.

Every detail had been arranged the day before; but the Swahili porter, as long as he is within reach of the drink-shops of the coast, is a mortal on whose action no reliable forecast can be based. A good many men were absent, and others paraded late; some objected to their loads, while others energetically seized a box or a bale and vanished into the surrounding jungle. Ultimately, after much noise and not a little unparliamentary language, the division marched off.

Having got the men started on their way to ford the narrow strip of water that created the island of Mombasa, the donkeys decided it was their turn to create trouble. At first none would move, then perversely all went at once and dashed at the narrow trail where an instant bottleneck was formed and in the mêlée half the loads were shed. Once order had been resumed and the convoy eventually set off again it was only to find that the tide had risen to cover the ford. They turned round and went home again. On Christmas Eve 1891 they finally left Mombasa. They encountered all the dangers and difficulties that might have been expected on such an expedition. The river route proved particularly gruelling, involving passing through mangrove swamps where the men at times had to wade chest deep. It was an impossible route for a railway: at its best the track was scarcely wide enough for the porters and their loads (the donkeys proved quite useless and had to be sent back to Mombasa). Where there was space to pitch a camp, it provided little comfort; one site was invaded by peculiarly vicious ants which bit the travellers so hard that the only remedy was to tear off the bodies and then extricate the still tightly embedded heads with knife or needle. But the greatest danger of all came from what must have been just about the last thing they expected – bees.

At the first attack by a swarm the porters fled in all directions, many badly stung. The bees were only driven off by heaping green wood on the fire to smoke them out. A second attack followed and once again there was general panic. This time one of the porters was stung so badly that he died. There was to be a third encounter. Macdonald had decided to climb the 5000-foot-high Nzoi peak. He and his party made their way up a narrow, steep ledge and discovered a nest close by the only route. They tried to creep past in their stockinged feet but the bees were disturbed – half the party turned and fled back down the path, the rest raced on up. All got away unscathed, but those who got to the summit discovered the unpleasant truth that the only way down was past the dreaded bees. They waited for nightfall and tiptoed down in the dark, with the unappealing prospect of bees on one side and a precipice on the other.

The expedition moved on and spent a good deal of time annihilating the local wildlife. One rhinoceros did its best to even the score by attacking the attackers, 'making for us like an express train.' Macdonald opted for the better part of valour and ran. They eventually succeeded in finding a likely route up the Kikuyu escarpment and this brought them into contact for the first time

213

with the warlike Masai. On an earlier expedition, led by Smith and Martin, one of Smith's assistants had clashed with the Masai and thirty of his party of a hundred had been killed. Macdonald's experience was a good deal less terrifying. Two porters had been dispatched to try and buy milk but had been chased off by warriors. They raced back to camp and now the Masai found themselves faced by an armed force and it was their turn to decamp, dropping two spears as they went. Macdonald recalled:

> Matters then adjusted themselves, and an amicable arrangement was made, by which they bound themselves to refrain from such national amusements as frightening porters, and we returned the spears to their owners.

Rather more dangerous attacks threatened the camp, but by using a portable searchlight and firing off powerful signal rockets, their nights were kept, if not quiet, at least safe.

At the end of it all, Macdonald, instead of having a peaceful time to write up his reports and prepare his maps, was called back to active service. He handed his notes and papers over to Pringle and went. Reading his account, written in the throwaway style of a laconic English gentleman, it is easy to be lulled into the impression that this is a typical Victorian or Edwardian adventure story. Yet this was a real expedition into virtually unknown, and certainly unmapped territory, with dangers from a hostile environment, disease, wild animals and a warlike population that did not take kindly to intruders. These men were not explorers setting off on some personal whim to uncover the secrets of the Dark Continent, but professional military engineers struggling to find a railway route where not even a road existed before.

By 1895 the days when private interests could control vast tracts of African land were coming to an end. The East African Company was disbanded and control passed to the government in London. Imperialism was at its zenith, but there was no lack of voices raised against further colonial expansion, and that included expansion via railway building. The opposition in the House of Commons in London was led by Henry Labouchere who saw the railway as a hopeless waste of money and a mere extension of colonialism, where there was nothing to be gained other than an enlarged red patch on the world map. He put his views bluntly: 'I trust there will remain Members of this House who will never bow the knee to King Jingo.' To the argument put forward by one of the railway's enthusiastic supporters that it offered great commercial opportunities, he had nothing but scorn. The only evidence he put forward, said Labouchere, was 'that some chief asked him when he left to be good enough to send him some opera glasses and white donkeys.' In spite of the biting rhetoric, the expansionists won the day, but the battle never ended: throughout the long and difficult years of construction the builders worked against a background of criticism from London and every request for funds brought a fresh bout of skirmishes. The Act was passed in 1896 and work on the Uganda Railway could officially begin.

The first necessity was a large workforce. Sir John Kirk, the vice-chairman, wrote,

We began by trying native labour, but we found we could not get enough of it to begin with, and then it would not go on continuously; that the natives, when the rains began, had to go back to their own gardens for the purpose of cultivation. Then came a time of famine owing to want of rain, and labour was almost impossible to get.

The company turned to India, but the Indian government laid down strict conditions: the men were to be paid proper wages and not on a piece-work basis, and at the end of the three-year contract they were to have a choice: to renew their contracts, to be sent home with all expenses paid or to remain as settlers. At first they were recruited by private firms in India, but later an official recruitment agency was set up in Bombay, the British East Africa and Nyasaland Agency. The first batch of 350 arrived in Mombasa in 1897 and by the time the line was finished, the records showed over 30,000 Indians had arrived to work on the railway. Labouchere's King Jingo certainly strutted these railway tracks. All Indians were known as coolies, whether they were unskilled or skilled, navvies or masons, clerks, surveyors or draughtsmen. As more men crowded in, the insanitary camps and bazaars spread, looked upon with contempt by European observers. Sir Frederick Jackson described the camps in the Nyando valley:

They were the most astounding examples of incompetence on the part of those responsible for their conduct, and for maintaining even a mild form of discipline. There were two in particular that I knew well, as they were more or less standing camps, between Lumbwa Station and the tunnel, and there was another near Fort Ternan. I passed them on foot, and that was enough: I never had the courage to walk through one. It was quite sufficient to view them from the line, well above, and only a few hundred yards away from them. Apart from the squalor, they were crowded with prostitutes, small boys and other accessories to the bestial vices so commonly practised by the Orientals. Complaints by the Nandi and Lumbwa natives were frequent, also by District Officers, but it was nobody's job to tackle the matter, until there were rumours of the Lumbwa becoming restive on account of so many of their young women being inveigled away from their homes, and harboured in these sinks of iniquity; then someone had the courage to clear out all the unattached hangers-on.

The account is not dissimilar to those written about the British navvies at work in England half a century earlier, but with the addition of racial prejudice. It is interesting to note that Sir Frederick was able to state quite clearly that all the women in the camp were prostitutes, when viewing them from 'a few hundred yards' away. That there was filth and disease in the camps is beyond dispute: the figures tell a tragic story. Of the 31,983 workers, 6454 had to be repatriated as invalids and 2943 died. The official reports also describe their work as 'most satisfactory' and no one ever questioned the view that without the 'coolies' the line could never have been built.

The difficulties were immense, and began as soon as work commenced. The first task was that of getting in supplies from Britain – 200,000 rails and a million sleepers together with their associated ironmongery. Supply trucks and locomotives arrived, the latter a disreputable array of pensioned-off old crocks from India of which the 0-6-0 F class were to prove the most reliable. In order to get them in at all, there had to be a major building programme to improve Mombasa harbour. It was a nightmare for the leading engineers, George Whitehouse, H. Patterson and Ronald Preston, who had to cope with the difficult terrain, atrocious climate, the ravages of disease and attacks by natives. Astonishingly, Preston's wife Florence came with him all the way, placidly embroidering and knitting at the entrance to her tent, and was to be rewarded by having the new terminus named in her honour, Port Florence. Perhaps she shared her husband's awe of the land through which they travelled. He wrote,

To describe what we saw in the way of game would be put down as exaggeration . . . it was nothing but a mass of hartebeeste, wildbeeste, zebra and the smaller antelope. The clang of rails and steel sleepers would frighten the game within about five hundred yards radius so as to make the number greater and denser at the edge of the circle.

Preston was in charge of the plate-laying gangs. The difficulties began straight away, as the annual report for 1896–7 makes clear:

Immediately on crossing the creek which divides Mombasa Island from the mainland, an abrupt rise begins. Range on range of low, thickly wooded hills succeed one another, and in the course of 15 miles the country rises 560 feet. From this point the country has proved to be more undulating than was expected. The thickness of the scrub continues and adds to the cost and time of completing the line. It is necessary to cut through miles of jungle, so heavy that it is often found impossible to do more than a quarter of a mile a day.

217

The monthly reports are a mixture of success and disaster.

October 1896 – Plate-laying was stopped until the viaduct could be crossed. It was completed on October 20th in twenty-five working days, a wonderfully expeditious performance . . . The total number of coolies was 2,689.

Nov 1896 – 27½ inches of rain fell during the month, and for twenty-two days no plate-laying was possible.

Dec 1896 – The rain was not so heavy, but a quarter of the coolies were in hospital. . .

Jan 1897 – Half the coolies were on the sick list.

One of the major problems, and one which contributed a great deal to the catalogue of sickness and disease, was the lack of fresh drinking water. The solutions sometimes proved worse than the problem. Water holes were choked with vegetation and slime. Preston's Indian servant suggested 'straining it through the end of his turban, saying they always did that with the water they drank, but I did not appreciate the turban filter.' His own preferred method was to add Eno's Fruit Salts, when the water would 'fizz up in hundreds of green bubbles, which on settling down left a thick green scum on top.' All he did then was to scoop off the scum and drink the water.

Problems were exacerbated by the lack of knowledge of the country among the senior engineers, and the general unhelpfulness of a system whereby the railway administrator had very little contact with the civil administrator. It was not unlike the system operated in the early years of Indian railways where ultimate decisions were in the hands of gentlemen in London, with the Secretary of State as the ultimate arbiter. Sir Charles Eliot, Commissioner of the East Africa Protectorate, saw the faults clearly.

The construction was supervised by a committee sitting in the Foreign Office, composed of distinguished gentlemen of wide experience, but in most cases that experience did not embrace railway work. Now, as one who has had an official connection with the Uganda Railway, I will venture to say that I have never known any class of questions as to which a man without technical knowledge is more hopelessly at sea than those presented by engineering and railway management.

There were men with local expertise. Ronald Hardy in researching his book on the Uganda Railway, *The Iron Snake*, unearthed the diary of Robert Turk, caravan leader, gunsmith and adventurer on whom Whitehouse came to rely for local knowledge. Up ahead lay one of the worst areas on the entire route: the Taru Desert. Water supply was the crucial factor, and Whitehouse proposed building a sea-water distillation plant at Mombasa and sending out water-supply trains to the advancing railhead. Turk was not impressed: 'God help him if his precious trains were late.' In the meantime, Turk agreed to lead the advance survey party across the desert. Walter Hearne, the surveyor, not only appeared incompetent but also clearly loathed and feared the African countryside. A missionary heading for the interior joined them. Things went wrong from the first. At the edge of the desert, six Wasoga bearers deserted taking water, food and a length of copper wire. Turk took a tracker and set off after them: he returned with four. He had shot the other two dead and now proceeded to have the unhappy quartet of survivors flogged and turned out of the camp. The episode did nothing to lift the gloom. Hearne now became ill, and in his delirious state wandered off into the desert. Turk, despite having been able to locate the six Wasoga, declared that there was no way of finding him. The missionary pleaded, but Turk remained obdurate. Finally the angry missionary set off on his own. When he failed to return, Turk was forced to set out at last to look for him. He found the missionary's dead body – but Hearne was never seen again.

Every element seemed to combine to slow up the crossing of the desert by the main platelaying gangs. Storms hit the region, undermining the little track that had been built. Whitehouse decided to withdraw in order to consolidate the line, thereby ensuring no further interruption in supplies. Turk was to push on

219

and establish a semi-permanent camp site at Tsavo where there was to be a big viaduct across the river, and where the river itself would act as a supply of clean water. Whitehouse declared that he would reach Tsavo in about three weeks. Time passed and no one appeared, so Turk went back to the desert to investigate. The situation was desperate. Water courses were completely dry; the water trains were not getting through, and real disaster struck when an embankment collapsed under a train killing twenty people. The desperate men went to the one known water hole, a former volcanic crater, but all it contained was the body of a leper floating in a sea of green slime. Hundreds of Indians joined Turk on the trek to Tsavo and water; seven died on the journey.

Everything about the desert was a nightmare. The area was covered with spiny shrubs that cut deep gashes in the Indians' bare legs. Flies laid eggs in the open wounds, which grew into blisters from which a huge maggot had to be squeezed out. The truck of the water train had no taps, so water had to be bailed out by the coolies, who paddled around, their ulcerated legs contaminating the water. The heat was intense. The wooden sleepers oozed hot creosote onto unprotected skin; the steel sleepers were so hot that bare feet became blistered. If the humans suffered, the pack animals fared even worse. This was tsetse fly country, and the mortality rate was appalling: 63 camels – all dead; 350 mules – 128 dead; 639 bullocks – 579 dead; 800 donkeys – 774 dead. It should have been an immense relief to reach the camp at Tsavo, but there a brand new terror awaited the men.

Lieutenant Colonel J.H. Patterson had come to Kenya specifically to oversee work on the bridge, though first he had to experience at first hand, as the other engineers on the route had done, the special character of the land through which this line was to pass. He records:

My first impression on coming out of my hut was that I was hemmed in on all sides by a dense growth of impenetrable jungle: and on scrambling to the top of a little hill close at hand, I found that the whole country as far as I could see was covered with low, stunted trees, thick undergrowth and 'wait-a-bit' thorns. The only clearing, indeed, appeared to be where the narrow track for the railway had been cut. This interminable *nyika*, or wilderness of whitish and leafless trees, presented a ghastly and sun-stricken appearance; and here and there a ridge of dark-red heat-blistered rock jutted out above the jungle, and added by its rugged barrenness to the dreariness of the picture. Away to the north-east stretched the unbroken line of the N'dungu Escarpment, while far off to the south I could just catch a glimpse of the snow-capped top of towering Kilima N'jaro.

Soon, however, work began on the bridge.

In a short time workmen and supplies came pouring in, and the noise of hammers and sledges, drilling and blasting, echoed merrily through the district.

A less merry noise was subsequently heard in the camp – the roar of two man-eating lions. The first encounter came when one of the lions burst into a tent where seven men were sleeping, grabbed one of them, a Sikh named Ungan Singh, by the throat and dragged him away while the others watched helpless. His dismembered body was found with only the head intact, eyes open and staring. As time went on, the lions grew ever bolder, leaping over or breaking through barriers. When the railhead moved on, leaving the bridge workers behind, the chances of being next on the lions' menu increased startlingly.

Patterson soon had other problems. He was not a popular man with the workforce, particularly when he substituted piece-rates for wages, contrary to the assurance given to the Indian government. His own explanation was that men had arrived, claiming to be skilled masons and demanding the extra rates to skilled men, when in fact they were imposters and cheats. There was a small riot and, more seriously, a plot to kill Patterson himself. He was lured into a narrow ravine where two men tried to grab him – rather half-heartedly it seems for he was able to push them off. He leapt onto a rock and spoke to the men in Hindi.

221

They all knew that I was just and fair to the real worker; it was only the scoundrels and shirkers who had anything to fear from me, and were upright, self-respecting Pathans going to allow themselves to be led away by men of that kind?

That was not to be the end of the trouble; the end only came when the ringleaders were arrested. Now the problems again centred on the lions.

The beasts hunted in pairs at night and became bolder all the time. One day several hundred men rushed out in front of a supply train, clambered on board and demanded to be taken away. Those that remained took elaborate precautions. Some dug pits inside their tents and covered them with logs, and there they slept through the sultry African night. Water towers were very popular, and 'every good-sized tree in the camp had as many beds lashed on it as its branches would bear – and sometimes more.' One tree collapsed under the weight; fortunately for its occupants, the lions had already fed. The District Officer, Mr Whitehead, was coming from the station down a narrow cutting when he was attacked and his sergeant carried off. Next day he was accosted by Patterson. He had gone looking for Whitehead, and found him looking 'very pale and ill'. Patterson recounts the conversation:

Where on earth have you come from?' I exclaimed. 'Why didn't you turn up to dinner last night?'
'A nice reception you give a fellow when you invite him to dinner,' was his only reply.
'Why, what's up?' I asked.
'That infernal lion of yours nearly did for me last night,' said Whitehead.
'Nonsense you must have dreamed it!' I cried in astonishment.
For answer he turned round and showed me his back. 'That's not much of a dream, is it?' he asked.
His clothing was rent by one huge tear from the nape of

222

the neck downwards, and on the flesh were four great claw
marks, showing red and angry through the torn cloth.

Patterson, an enthusiastic hunter, waged war on the lions. He
tried everything, including building a huge trap with two coolies
as bait. They were at the far end of the cage, 'safe' behind bars.
The idea was that the lion would come in and they would shoot
it: a lion did come in and the terrified men shot almost everything
in sight except their target, which escaped. They almost shot
Patterson – and one would hardly have blamed them if they had.
In the end however he was able to bag the lions and work proceeded more or less as normal.

Patterson was then sent off to establish a headquarters for
railway administrators. The spot selected was on an empty plain
'three hundred and twenty-seven miles from the nearest place
where even a nail could be purchased . . . Roads and bridges had
to be constructed, houses and work-shops built, turn-tables and
station quarters erected, a water supply laid on, and a hundred
and one other things done which go to the making of a railway
township.' A bazaar soon mushroomed, but disease broke out
and Patterson had it all torn down. The railway headquarters was
destined to become the civil headquarters as well and was to grow
to become the city of Nairobi. When Whitehouse arrived at
Nairobi he found the local population on the verge of starvation.
He handed out his railway supplies but as news spread more and
more people crowded in. Whitehouse was in despair.

Why is it *our* responsibility? We are building a railway. We
are not a relief organisation. These poor people must be
helped but I have fifteen thousand coolies to feed.

He decided it was the government's job not his, and stopped
the relief. The inevitable result was that the Africans began a
series of raids.

They several times swooped down on isolated railway
maintenance gangs and utterly annihilated them in order to

223

obtain possession of the food which they knew would be stored in the camps.

They attacked at night using poisoned arrows, but Turk was on hand to exact his customary rough retribution. He attacked the native village: 'We shot two or three but they were half dead from starving and the pox.' Even he complained that food would have done more good than bullets. Eventually government relief arrived, ending the whole miserable affair.

The engineers also had some daunting problems of a purely engineering nature to face. The line that had begun at sea level at Mombasa was to climb to a height of 8700 feet, where the heat of the plain was replaced by ice and sleet driven by a howling wind. And it also had to cross the Great Rift Valley. There was a fall here of 2000 feet, and the escarpment had to be conquered, as others had been elsewhere in the world, by a complex zig-zagging route of steep gradients. For actual construction pur-poses, inclines were used, worked by stationary engines. Even then the slopes were so steep that material tipped out of the wagons; special wheeled frames had to be built, with a triangular frame, so that one set of wheels was higher than the other. Once set on the incline, the platform was level and could carry a con-ventional truck on top. Even with the inclines, work was extra-ordinarily difficult. 'No. 2 Incline was so steep', wrote Preston, 'that the workmen, even empty-handed, could hardly keep their feet.'

Far from being empty-handed they were manhandling rails and sleepers into place in situations where a slip could send them plunging as much as 400 feet down a precipice. On the approach to the Mau summit, a total of twenty-seven viaducts were built, ranging from 156–881 feet in length and from 37–111 feet high. At last, five years and nearly 600 miles from the start, the lines reached Lake Victoria. Florence Preston drove home the last key and gave her name to the terminus.

This was not the last line to be built by the British in Africa. As late as the 1920s, they were working with the Portuguese to create the Benguela Railway, stretching right across Angola from

Lobito on the coast to the Congo frontier, 838 miles away. Much of the rolling stock came from Britain. The African dream was never quite realized: the direct line from the Cape to Cairo was never completed, but there was a true element of heroism in what was achieved. The gangs run by the indefatigable Pauling even made it into the age of the cine-camera. The last half mile of the Rhodesia route to Broken Hill was filmed by Pathe, and the platelayers worked so fast that the train carrying the rails was never actually brought to a standstill. It somehow typifies the world of African railways that although the movie camera was by then in use, railway building was still down to human muscle and brawn.

CHAPTER SEVEN

Australasia

In 1849 the *Melbourne Herald* listed the benefits that railways would bring to Australia:

No more sticking in the mud then, no more badgering about the condition of the roads, no losing of bullocks, nor plundering of bullock-drivers, no leaving grain in the ground to rot, or wool on the way to spoil with rain, no escaping of prisoners under escort, no stopping the mail by bushrangers, no being at the mercy of servants for want of change, no dying for want of a doctor, no broomstick marriages for want of a priest, and no loss of time, money and patience, by detention in town, beyond the time absolutely required for the want of business.

If it does rather overstate the case for the virtues of rail travel, then it was doing no more than many another polemic on the subject had done in the past, and would do again in the future. What is remarkable is how little time had passed since the first settlers arrived in the colony before this absolute need for a rail system was perceived. It was only in January 1788 that the first convict ship dropped anchor in Botany Bay and a small party sailed north and discovered 'the finest harbour in the world'. The description was Arthur Phillip's, a retired naval officer who had been appointed Governor-in-Chief of New South Wales. He called the natural harbour Sydney Cove. Phillip had come to oversee a penal colony; there was little thought of trade. Future prosperity and transport meant little more than the packing off of prisoners from Britain. The indigenous population had no roads, no bridges. No one knew what lay in the interior, no one had even the faintest idea how big the place was. It was only with the first circumnavigation in 1802–3 the settlers became aware that this was not a country, but a vast continent. It is a mark of the extraordinary vigour that characterized Australian development that it took little more than half a century from tentative beginnings in an unknown land before the settlers were demanding railways, the most potent symbols of the modern world of commerce and industry.

The argument over convicts was to last for forty of those years: should they work for free settlers or for the government? Would they ever be allowed the same rights as freemen? What status would their children have? These were serious issues in the strangely unbalanced county of New South Wales, which in 1828 was recorded as having a total population of 36,598 of whom 16,442 were convicts and only 1544 women. The other pressing problem was one of how to prosper in the new land. In 1813, three explorers – Blaxland, Wentworth and Lawson – found a route through the Blue Mountains and looked out on a seemingly endless plain of good grazing land. One answer to future wealth had been found – sheep. And all the time the settlement was expanding. In the 1830s plans were laid for a new settlement in the Cape St Vincent area. The South Australian Land Company was formed and in 1834 South Australia became a province in its own right, with a capital at Adelaide. It was in New South Wales and South Australia that the railway movement began.

Although the two provinces had their own governments, there was a general understanding that it made sense to work towards a unified railway system for the whole country. In 1848 the two legislatures took the obvious step of settling for 4 ft. 8½ inches on the rational grounds that as Australia had no manufacturing industry of its own, everything needed for railway building would be brought across from Britain, and life would be simpler, and cheaper, if the principal British gauge was used. The argument, indeed, seems so sensible that it is difficult to see what could be

227

said against it, and it had the strong support of the Secretary of State for War and the Colonies, William Gladstone. He reinforced the argument by pointing to the mayhem of the gauge war in England. Nor were there other serious precedents to follow in Australia. There was a tramway, built on the English model, that carried, appropriately enough, coal from the mines to Newcastle on the coast; and Tasmania had a wooden railway which at a shilling a time took passengers across the Tasman Peninsula to Port Arthur penal settlement. The former used gravity for power, and the latter used convicts, who pushed uphill and acted as human brakes going downhill. Neither of these needed to have much influence on the rational planning of a national steam railway system. Everything seemed set fair for a period of logical development. Then the Sydney Railway Company appointed F.W. Shields as chief engineer.

Shields was an Irishman who had worked with Vignoles. He took the view that in an overcrowded little island like Britain, the modest gauge of 4 ft. 8½ in. might be adequate, but with all the vast spaces of Australia to build in, a more generous view could be taken. He persuaded the Board to adopt the Irish gauge of 5 ft. 3 in. South Australia, willing to be accommodating, went along with the change, and put in orders for locomotives and rolling stock. In the meantime, the Sydney Company found itself short of funds and asked Shields to take a cut in salary. Grievously offended, Shields at once resigned and his place was taken by the Scottish engineer, James Wallace, who was as devout a believer in the Stephenson gauge as Shields had been in the Irish. Plans were reassessed in Sydney and New South Wales, but neighbouring Victoria and South Australia had already invested heavily in the 5 ft. 3 in. gauge and were in no mood for expensive changes. The war that Gladstone had warned against had come about. To make matters worse, when Queensland began building lines, much later on in the 1860s, it was decided that cash was paramount, and they opted for a cheap 3 ft. 6 in., also well fitted to the difficult terrain. Australia ended up, like India, with three systems, broad, standard and narrow. No doubt it all made sense at the time.

In the 1850s, the whole nature of railway building, and of

228

Australian society as a whole, changed very suddenly. A digger called E. Hargraves came to Australia from California and thought the landscape very like that of the gold fields he had recently left behind. He found gold and set off a gold rush that led to the discovery of the great alluvial deposits at Ballarat. Everyone, it seemed, headed for the gold fields – even sea captains could be seen at work; they had little choice since their crews had already deserted. For a time there was no labour for railway building, but in the long term it brought a flood of immigrants. The new Australians felt quite able to settle the land for themselves and neither needed, nor wanted, convict labour. Hence the transportation of convicts came to a halt. The immigrants did, however, need better transport, to serve both the gold fields and the rapidly growing communities.

Once the first excitement of the gold rush had died down, railway work was resumed. The broad gauge track was first in use when 2 miles of track was opened from Melbourne to Port Melbourne. It was hurried along in order to get supplies to the goldfield. A year later, the 13-mile route from Sydney to Parramatta followed. The Sydney line was not a huge success and was taken over by the state, renamed the Great Western Railway and gradually extended westward to the foot of the Blue Mountains. John Whitton arrived from England in 1857 as chief engineer for all the New South Wales lines; he was to stay on in Australia to oversee more than 2000 miles of track construction, including an amazing 289 miles in one year. There would have been no possibility of building at such a rate with the meagre supplies of local labour, and Whitton turned, as so many others had done, to Thomas Brassey.

Brassey himself never went to Australia, but handed the job to one of his agents, Samuel Wilcox, who had worked with him on the Paris and Caen Railway. Wilcox set off for New South Wales in 1859. At first local men were taken on at wages varying from 7s. a day for labourers to 12s. for skilled tradesmen. It was considered a very generous wage. Wilcox was closely questioned on the standard of living by Brassey's biographer, Arthur Helps:

Q. Take a man spending 10s. a week there; if he had been living in England would it have cost him 8s.?

A. He would get as much bread and meat there as he could eat, but here he could hardly look at it. As long as a man with a family is kept from drink there, he can, in a very short time, get sufficient money to start and buy a piece of land, and become 'settled'.

Q. May it not be said that a good stout labourer in England could not live as a navvy for less than 8s. a week?

A. Not living as a navvy does. I do not think that he could live on 8s. a week; living generously as a navvy has to live. Out there he could live very much more amply supplied at 10s., and really on less than 10s. In the case of some of the men I have known camping out together, the rations did not come to more than 8s. 6d. per week.

Unfortunately, the rosy picture of independent labourers saving up for their own land does not take account of the navvies' habit of taking the occasional tipple.

Q. Did you find that a working man, placed as he appears to be in Australia in exceptionally advantageous positions with regards to means, drinks more?

A. Yes; he does.

Q. In short, there is a great deal of drunkenness there?

A. Yes; and the drink is more expensive; they charge you more there; they charge you 6d. for a glass of beer, and they charge for a bottle of beer 2s. 6d., which you get for 1s. in England.

It was soon obvious that more men were needed, and Brassey sent his recruiting agents to Scotland. This was a period when the government was trying to encourage emigration, so that Brassey fitted the men out at an average cost of £5 each, while the government contributed a further £12 for the passage. Brassey had no contract with the men, but was on pretty firm ground as Wilcox explained:

Having men in the country, we knew that they must work for
somebody; and we also knew that we were in a position to
pay them as much as, or more than, any one else. They were
at liberty, on landing, to go where they liked; and some few,
not a great number, but some few, never came to the works
at all; but we found that we got a great part of them, and
more came out by other ships.

Initially, Brassey helped pay for 2000 Scots to travel to Australia.

Whitton having pushed the route on to the foot of the Blue
Mountains was faced with a climb to the ridge at 3336 feet – not
something where his experience on the Oxford, Worcester and
Wolverhampton Railway would be of a great deal of use. Early
suggestions were for a charge up the mountain at the ludicrous
slope of 1 in 20, later modified to a rather more modest 1 in 30,
though that was only possible if a 2-mile tunnel was blasted half
way up the mountain. In the end, Whitton settled for a zigzag
which involved the construction of a large number of viaducts and
the blasting away of vast quantities of rock. The largest single
mass, estimated at 45,000 tons, was reduced to rubble by an explosion detonated by the Countess of Belmore, wife of the Governor-
General. Thanks to the zigzag, with its two reverses, a very
reasonable 1 in 60 was maintained, but it gave spectacular views
as the track made its way to the summit up a narrow, spiny ridge.
Having got to the top, there was no comfortable plateau, but
instead a switchback ride over the mountains, before plunging down the other side in the even more exciting Lithgow
zigzag.

Railway building in Australia was not a question so much of
joining centres of population as of pushing out a route into the
wilderness which settlers could follow. One English engineer at
least was unimpressed by the process. C.O. Burge had moved on
from working in India (see Chapter 5) and arrived to work in New
South Wales, surveying a new route. 'The district was one which
was called populous, yet on the whole of about thirty miles of the
proposed railway there was only one squatter.' Conversation was
less than amusing: 'If you cannot talk sheep, you are out of it.'

And when he did reach towns, he found them even less impressive than the outback.

Our next move was to an up-country township to take charge of the construction of another line; and here I would remark that, having seen since a vast number of Australian country towns, the deadly, drab, dull similarity of one to the other I never saw equalled except in a sack of peas. At a later period, some of my duties involved fixing the site of new townships in the then uninhabitable Bush at suitable distances on projected railways, and as they were to be on the terrible chessboard plan, and would no doubt be built in the usual formal style, my artistic conscience must bear the weight of having assisted in the extension of such hideousness. The style consists of straight wide streets, flanked with brick barrack-like houses roofed with corrugated iron, with verandahs painted with yellow and red stripes covering the footways, and supported by posts at edge of the latter, the court house, banks and hotels being slightly more pretentious than the ordinary shops.

Lines were soon spreading south as well as west out of Sydney, while at the same time the broad gauge routes were developing in Victoria. Here work proved even more difficult than it had in New South Wales, with conditions more like those of the jungles of Africa. Thomas Griffin surveyed one 14-mile stretch of line: the work was to take him two whole years. He had to carve a way through almost impenetrable undergrowth, hacking through dense forest and clearing fallen trees. The land was impossible for pack animals, so everything had to be carried on the survey party's backs. In 1883 the routes from Victoria and New South Wales met at Albury, when for the first time the inconveniences of a break of gauge made itself felt. Everything, passengers and freight, had to be moved from one train to the other. In 1887, the Victoria and South Australian Railways were also united.

There was still one gap to be filled in New South Wales. The line running north from Sydney stopped at the Hawkesbury River.

Here passengers were ferried across on an aged stern-wheeled paddle steamer. After that they could continue on their journey north to Newcastle and Queensland. There had already been a number of iron bridges built in Australia, which had been designed and prefabricated in Britain. The Murray Bridge, for example, was designed by the UK consultant William Dempsey with ironwork supplied from Crumlin in Ebbw Vale. However, rather as the Canadians had done, the Australians began to have doubts as to whether the British were always the best people to turn to for design. Other countries, notably America, had conditions much more similar to those of Australia: the bush has more in common with the prairie than it has with the neatly hedged fields of Surrey. Not only that but the collapse of the Tay Bridge in 1878 severely dented the old country's reputation for unmatched excellence. It was Henry Mais, a Bristolian who had begun his working life on the GWR, who encouraged the spread of American techniques. He had come to Australia in 1850. After a somewhat varied career in New South Wales – resigning from the Sydney Railway Company in 1852 and being sacked from the Sydney waterworks for gross misconduct – he moved to Victoria. As part of his railway work, he undertook a world tour to look at how others were tackling production problems. He returned full of enthusiasm for American ideas, and these notions soon spread through the Australian engineering community.

When it came to the Hawkesbury River crossing, the work was put out to international tender, with a very distinguished committee vetting the applicants. These included W.H. Barlow who was responsible for the second – successful – Tay Bridge and Sir John Fowler of the Forth Bridge and the Severn Tunnel. They awarded the contract to the Union Bridge Company of New York. Even so many parts ended up being made in Britain, and C.O. Burge was appointed as one of the resident engineers in charge of the work on site. It was certainly an imposing affair, with seven spans, each of 410 feet, and a total length of 2896 feet. Furthermore, space had to be allowed for small steamers to pass underneath. Burge and his associates were faced with the problem of making piers that had to go down through 40 feet of water, after which instead of reaching a good solid foundation they met mud, over 100 feet of it. The traditional method of making a coffer dam, pumping it out and building the pier inside, was clearly impossible. Instead they decided to make a 150-foot high cylinder on the bank, sink it down through the mud and fill it with concrete. This was easier said than done: there was no way a tube of that size could be towed out, raised to the vertical and sent straight down. No system then available could control the accurate movement of such a huge structure through swirling water and cloying mud and then settle it down with perfect accuracy. The whole operation would have to be carried out a section at a time: sink one bit, add another on top, sink that and so on. Burge explained how it worked in practice:

To understand the shape of the caisson and the operation of sinking it, the reader should imagine for the bottom length a top hat without its crown and brim, and inside it three vertical tubes each about the diameter, proportionally to the hat, of a small coffee-cup. Unlike the cup, however, the tubes must be supposed to be bottomless and splaying out like a trumpet-mouth below, so as to meet the bottom edge of the hat, forming a sharp edge. Such, on a very large scale, was the bottom length, or shoe as it is called, of the caisson. This shoe was floated out slightly weighted with concrete, to the exact site of the pier for which it was destined, and from the hold of a ship anchored alongside, more concrete in a liquid state was poured into the space between the outside of the tubes and the sides of the caisson, the weight of this concrete causing the shoe to sink to the bottom of the river. This done, the next thing was to get the structure down through the mud, and in order to do this, the mud had to be got out of its way. It was for this purpose that the tubes were provided which, it will have been noted, were as yet not filled with the concrete which was all round them. Specially shaped dredging buckets, or grabs as they are called, were then let down inside the tubes, and from their peculiar action forced their massive jaws into the mud and drew it up by means of steam hoists, this going incessantly day and night concurrently with the concrete filling and weighting, until the great mass was sent down to its final resting-place, in one case 162 feet below the water-line. The tubes, which were, of course, built up simultaneously with the sides of the caisson, were then filled with concrete, so that there was a solid mass of this material from the hard bottom up to the water-level, upon which the stone piers above water were subsequently built. In this bridge, therefore, what is visible to the spectator, large as that is, is only about half of the entire structure, the other half being sunk under water.

The hardest part was manoeuvring the caisson into position. On one occasion the giant cylinder was caught by a sudden rising wind. The tugs could not hold it and it set off majestically for the open sea: fortunately the wind dropped, more tugs were called up and the errant caisson retrieved. Having finally got it into position over the spot it still had to be sunk with considerable accuracy, as girders each 410 feet long and a thousand tons in weight then had to be set in place on the bearings at the top. Even when that was achieved, the girders themselves still had to be raised into position. Once again the usual practice of erecting a temporary timber staging between the piers was useless thanks to the deep mud and fast currents. Burge goes on:

The plan adopted was to construct and float in shallow water adjoining the shore an immense pontoon of timber, somewhat less in length than a span of the bridge, and to erect on it a scaffolding up to the same height above low tide as the top of the bridge piers were over low water. This done, while still at the moorings along the shore, the girders were put together on the top of the scaffolding with their ends projecting. When this was complete, and when a favourable condition of wind and current existed, the great craft with its top-heavy load was towed out by a sufficient number of steamers to the span for which that particular pair of girders was destined. The operation was so timed that on arrival

235

between the piers high water would occur. The whole construction would then gradually sink with the falling tide until the projecting ends of the girders rested in their places on the pier, and the pontoon and staging sinking further would become free from their great load and be towed back to shore to serve the same purpose for the other sets of girders – seven in all.

This was anxious work, but only once did the whole process almost end in disaster, with the span nearest the shore at the southern end.

The pontoon with its load was successfully navigated to near the site, and all was going merrily as a wedding bell, when great delay occurred in trying to warp her round. The hitherto rising tide had begun to turn, and before the manoeuvre was complete one end of the pontoon got aground on a sunken rock, the rest of it being in deep water. For many hours all efforts to draw her off failed – efforts stimulated by the possible serious consequences of failing to do so, for with the tide still falling the floating end would gradually sink more and more, the other end remaining stationary; and unless the slope at low tide was still insufficient to cause it, the great girders of one thousand tons weight would slip off into the deep river. In such case they would be utterly lost, not only by smashing themselves to pieces, but by being sunk in one hundred feet of mud, and nothing that could be done would have held them back. Moreover, if the whole vessel with its load had slipped off, destruction would equally have occurred, as the top-heavy character of the loading was only suitable for quiet movement, and not for the violent plunge downwards into the water which this result would have caused. The loss in a moment of time would have been enormous, besides causing serious delay in the opening of the bridge. The engineers and contractors' representatives stood by on shore absolutely helpless, only trusting in the possibility of the tide turning before the steepness of the

inclination of the girders would have been too much for their
stability. Their hearts almost stood still as the time for low
tide indicated by the almanac approached. The situation
seemed desperate; great creaks and groans were heard as if
the mighty structure was straining all its muscles, so to speak,
to save itself, when, just as it was thought that all was over,
the witching time of low tide arrived, the crisis was passed,
and the girders still held fast. A few inches less of water and
the newspaper posters of the world would have been blazoned
with the disaster. As the tide rose, the pontoon again lifted
itself level, and when high water occurred she was afloat end
to end, and was safely brought into position.

Even at this distance in time, reading Burges' account still
makes one gasp in astonishment at the sheer audacity of the plan.
In the mind's eye one can see the tottering array of scaffolding with
its massive load being edged out into a fast-flowing river to be
positioned with inch-perfect accuracy between the tall piers. It is
amazing that anyone could conceive of such a plan – even more
amazing that it worked.

Burge went on from Hawkesbury to look for new railway
routes, often through the most difficult territory. In one section
he had to cut through scrub hung with creepers that clung
tenaciously to the traveller and drew blood: the Australians called
them 'lawyers'. His first journey was of 640 miles, during which
he was trapped for a week by floods, marooned in a pub. As well
as deciding on a line, he also had to find station sites. At one stop
the local mayor asked if he could call with a delegation. Burge
waited, but no one came. The next day the mayor sent an apology.
They had stopped off for a beer *en route* and it was, of course,
unthinkable that they should move on until everyone had bought
a round. There were fourteen in the delegation. On the whole,
Burge seems to have enjoyed his time in Australia.

To the north of the Hawkesbury River in Queensland, engineers
found quite different problems to those that faced the pioneers
of Sydney. Brisbane had only been founded in 1824 and here,
500 miles away from Sydney at the edge of the huge, virtually

unopened spaces of the Northern Territory, thoughts of gauge breaks and unified systems must have been far from anyone's mind. There was, however, once again an imperative for building, with the discovery of gold in the Golden Mile that stretched from Kalgoorlie to Boulder. Fitzgibbon, the first engineer to consider the problem, suggested a narrow gauge, but it was his successor W.T. Doyne, who had worked with Brassey in the Crimea, who successfully argued the case. He began by setting out quite frankly that the proposed 3 ft. 6 in. gauge was second best. It would mean less powerful locomotives and a poorer surface, but he then went on with admirable pragmatism to argue the case that second best is a good deal better than nothing at all.

The position of Queensland appears to me to be simply this. It possesses a great territory inland which is cut off from the ports on the seaboard by mountain ranges, which have to be crossed by any system of communications which may be adopted. The present means of the colony are inadequate to provide a system of broad-gauge railways, while the wants of the community demand some power superior to the bush-tracks of transit. A medium course has, therefore, been introduced – I think, wisely. A railway is being constructed at a moderate cost which will amply meet the needs of this community for many years to come, which is perfect as far as its powers extend, and will, I have no doubt, act as a pioneer to develop the resources of the colony, and enable it to carry out superior works when necessity demands them, without having in the first instance loaded it with the incubus of debt which would retard its progress in other matters.

Peto and Betts were to take one contract in Queensland for a line across the Great Dividing Range from Ipswich to Toocoombs. The consultant engineer was Sir Charles Fox, with Abram Fitzgibbon as the man on the spot. It was a fierce line of steep grades – up to 1 in 54 – tight turns and the long Victoria tunnel to pierce the summit ridge. Hardware and structures of all kinds, including prefabricated stations, were sent out from England,

238

together with locomotives and rolling stock. By now, however, there was a local labour force available, and 800 men were recruited from inside Australia. The engineers complained, as engineers always did, of poor work and slow work, but the line was ready in three years. Local men could do the job – and in future no Queensland contracts were to go to England. Australians could build their own railways.

Australia prided itself on being, and proved to be, a land of opportunities for individuals with the energy and drive to grab them. Richard Speight came to Australia in 1864 as a railway administrator and engineer after an early career spent on the Midland Railway in England. A stout, balding, heavily bearded man, he appeared the very model of Victorian probity and respectability; yet he used his post in Melbourne to please venal politicians rather than to serve the public. He built a station at a cost of £4000 to serve a country racecourse where no race was ever held. He ran an express train from Melbourne to Bendigo though there was never the remotest chance of there being enough people wanting to visit Bendigo to make it pay. But the politicians of Bendigo were pleased – and showed it. Friends and relations of prominent men were given jobs and when they were fired for incompetence, Speight took them on again. His land purchases were notorious, paying as much as ten times the true value. The press became ever more vociferous, until at last he was forced to resign. Even then the company paid him £5250 in compensation, which he promptly used to sue the papers that had brought him low. He paid out around £3000 in legal fees and, in a hearing that lasted 86 days in September 1894, he received the judgment in his favour. It was a sorry triumph: the jury awarded him one farthing in damages and no costs. It was a squalid episode in the otherwise decent tradition of British railway building in Australia.

Tasmania offered an even more mountainous terrain than the worst of mainland Australia so that when the Launceston and Western Railway Company began to build the first line they had no hesitation in opting for the 3 ft. 6 in. gauge. The line, opened in 1871, set the standard for the island, though in the very worst areas the gauge was dropped to 2 ft. Hauling heavy trains on

239

narrow gauge tracks was a problem that troubled operators the world over. It was the very nature of such lines that they would have tight curves which would seem to rule out the use of big, powerful locomotives. A solution occurred to the inspecting engineer for New South Wales, William Garratt. His design called for an articulated locomotive with two power units fed by the boiler. The result looked as if the designer had begun with a conventional locomotive with driving cab, boiler and chimney, with the only difference being the positioning of the cylinders at the back, under or behind the cab. There, however, convention ended, for in front of this was a strange assemblage, with a second power unit and a further set of cylinders. The first design called for a 2-4-0 + 0-4-2 wheel arrangement. There was plenty of power, and the locomotive could 'bend' in the middle where the extra power unit was attached. Garratt came to England and showed his designs to Beyer, Peacock of Manchester. They developed the design commercially, and the very first Garratts were sold to Tasmania for use on the 2 feet line in 1909.

The Garratt proved an immense success, not only in Tasmania but on narrow-gauge railways throughout the world. A series of tests in South Africa in 1921 showed it to pull heavier loads at higher speeds than its rivals, including the majestic compound Mallet. The tester noted tersely, 'The Mallet is 46 tons heavier than the Garratt and pulls less'. Weight was very important on the light track often used in poorer countries, and, being articulated, the Garratt could spread the load over a large number of axles. The Kenya and Uganda was supplied with immense 4-8-4 + 4-8-4 engines, giving a total of 16 axles to bear the weight. Garratts could also be built for speed. Tasmania was once again the testing ground in 1912 for the early high-speed Garratts, this time for use on the 3 ft. 6 in. line. A 4-4-2 + 2-4-4 engine, with four cylinders on each bogie, achieved a speed of 55 m.p.h. which is good going on a narrow gauge track.

If Tasmania presented problems, then a contour map of New Zealand looks like the design for a railway engineer's nightmare. It is every bit as bad as it looks, so bad, in fact, that although at its narrowest South Island is scarcely a hundred miles across there was no rail connection between the east and west coasts until 1925, and that was only made possible by boring the 5½-mile Otira tunnel. It was not only the difficult, mountainous country that made for slow railway development – the development of settlements was equally tardy. Although James Cook had arrived in 1769, by 1835 there were still only 2000 Europeans in the entire country. Official colonization acts set up Wellington and Nelson in 1840, Otago in 1848 and Canterbury in 1850. The infant settlements, however, did show an early enthusiasm for railways.

Construction started in South Island. In the 1850s, work began on a road to link the port of Lyttelton to the interior, and construction had hardly got under way before critics were saying that it would have been more sensible to build a railway. These first railway rumblings were heard just four years after the colony had been officially founded. Not to be outdone, the citizens of Wellington on North Island began agitating for a line to link them to the interior. But it needed more than the clamour of a handful of possible passengers to justify the expense. Freight was to supply the demand. In 1852, the settlers at Nelson in the north-west corner of South Island began exploring Dun Mountain and found promising deposits of copper ore. In 1854, W.L. Wrey came to London to raise capital for a mining venture. When he returned to New Zealand with the cash, he soon found himself being given the job of raising more money, this time for a railway from mine to port.

The parent company, the Dun Mountain Copper Mining Company, was incorporated in London and this time it seemed a good idea for someone to go out from England to visit the works. The man given the task was Thomas Hackett who found that the miners were looking for the wrong mineral: the copper deposits were disappointing but there were good supplies of chrome. Chromium compounds were widely used in printing coloured patterns for the textile industry. The copper mine became a chrome mine and the company approved the railway which was given official blessing by the Nebou Provincial Council in 1858. Rails, iron sleepers and wagons were sent over from England, to be followed in 1860 by W.T. Doyne, already mentioned for his

241

work in Australia, and G.C. Fitzgibbon who had worked in Canada and Ceylon. The start of work was held up by the central government whose sluggish deliberations meant that final approval was not given until 1861. Officially, this was a railway designed for use by steam locomotives; in actuality, it was an old-fashioned tramway. The easiest gradient was 1 in 76 and for nine miles it was a precipitous 1 in 20. The 3-foot double track was initially worked as a system down which loaded trucks descended under gravity and empties were hauled back up by horses. Whether in time it might have been made over to steam, as similar lines – such as the Festiniog – had been in Britain, will never be known. The little line had hardly got started when Civil War broke out in America, the supply of cotton for the mills of Lancashire dried up and the demand for chromium dyes disappeared. The mine and its railway were closed and there was still no steam locomotive in New Zealand. It had, however, shown that railways could be built in the country and when the Wellington Council began investigating the possibilities of promoting a line, they specified one 'similar to the Dun Mountain Railway', though they did increase the gauge to 3 ft. 6 in. and envisaged locomotives being used from the very beginning. They made a declaration that epitomized the reasoning behind railway building in South America, Canada, Africa, in fact everywhere that aspired to extend settlement out into the wild countryside: 'Let the country but make the railroads, and the railroads will make the country.'

The next development came at Christchurch. The port was at Lyttelton Harbour separated from the town by the Lyttelton Port Hills. The road had been built in 1852 and the provincial government had been pushed into making a promise that, at the very least, they would give serious consideration to a railway as soon as funds permitted. Local businessmen led by William Moorhouse – who earned himself the nickname 'Railway Billy' – began arguing ever more urgently for a railway to speed up development of the settlement. In 1858, the transport commissioners bowed to the pressure and wrote to Robert Stephenson to ask if he would take on the job. By then Stephenson's ill health had caused him to give up virtually all railway work – he was to die in 1859 – but he recommended his nephew, George Robert Stephenson, for the job. Stephenson went out to New Zealand to survey the difficult route which included a tunnel through hard rock. It was to be built to the Australian broad gauge of 5 ft. 3 ins. At this stage no one seemed to be thinking very seriously about standardization – so far three railways had proposed three gauges, 3 ft., 3 ft. 6 in. and 5 ft. 3 in. Looking at this mountainous country as a whole, no one could surely expect to cover it with the wider gauge lines, but then, who would have expected a Stephenson of all people to appear as a champion of the broad gauge! The contract was given to Smith and Knight of Westminster, but when they arrived and took test borings along the line of the tunnel, they immediately asked for the price to be increased from £235,000 to £265,000. Stephenson refused, and the contract went instead to Holme and Co. of Melbourne. When one considers that railway building in Australia was very much in its infancy, this was a bold decision. The experienced British contractor had said that no profit could be made at the old price given the nature of the rock through which the tunnel had to be driven. Events were to suggest it was a wise decision.

Progress on the tunnel was desperately slow: 50 yards a month at the very best, a paltry 10 yards at the worst. They were destined to slave away in the hills for years. No one was prepared to wait for ever, so a temporary line was opened from a riverside wharf at Ferrymead. It helped in providing a supply route to the tunnel and enabled the New Zealand railway system to open its first steam service. On 6 May 1863 the first locomotive was delivered from Slaughter, Gruning & Co. of Bristol. It was a simple 2-4-0 tank engine, the very model of good British design from its shining brass dome to its 6-foot-diameter drive wheels, but differentiated from its English cousins by the broad spark-arrester chimney, an essential feature of all wood-burning locomotives. Still, however, the men slaved away in the tunnel which was not opened until 1867.

Meanwhile, the line was being extended north and south along the coast from Canterbury, crossing two broad rivers in the process, the Raikaie and the Rangitate, and acquiring a new and suitably grand name, the Canterbury Great Southern Railway. By 1870, the route to the north was open as far as the Selwyn River, and a certain amount of work had been done to the south of Canterbury. But this early experiment in broad gauge construction was to be short-lived: the pioneering line from Ferrymead, the first to open, was also the first to close. It was a muddled time, when no one knew quite what to do. There was no lack of enthusiasm in New Zealand, but there was a great lack of experience. The young country was open to new ideas, but was not always able to distinguish between the innovative and the eccentric. In 1863, an American engineer, J.R. Davies, demonstrated a cost-saving railway using native timber instead of imported iron. The locomotive literally blazed down the tracks, the sparks from the engine leaving a trail of burning rails behind it. All very entertaining, but not very helpful in building up a sound railway system, and it was not until the 1870s that a really solid basis for expansion was established. What was needed were not wild, innovative ideas but a realizable vision of the future. That needed a man who could combine imagination and practicality. New Zealand found such a man in Julius Vogel.

Vogel had left London to join the great gold rush to Victoria and had then moved on to New Zealand where he became involved in politics, and ended up as government treasurer. What he proposed was a rail-building system far more ambitious than anything tried in any other developing country. The government should pump money into construction, and as soon as lines were open use the revenue to pay for still more building. His plan was to borrow £10 million over a period of ten years, using the public land along the new transport routes as security. There was to be nothing fancy about the programme. It could all be summed up in one simple phrase: get as far as possible as cheaply as possible. This was the old cry again. Expand the railway, open up the country and you encourage immigration: ' . . . the railroads will make the country'. Given the usual reaction of politicians and authority to innovative ideas, the surprise is that he was not only listened to, but his advice was largely followed. A public works department was established, a general Railways Act was passed, authorizing the new department to raise money and, somewhat belatedly, a Gauge Bill was introduced that would settle the gauge for future railways in the country. Almost equally surprising was the fact that the local politicians freely admitted their ignorance of railway affairs and turned to the English engineers, Charles Fox and Son for practical advice. They recommended the Australian narrow gauge of 3 ft. 6 in. which they already had experience of building. The advice was accepted, even though it meant tearing up the existing track and relaying it. At least New Zealand now had a national standard, putting the country one up on its larger neighbour.

Vogel began by promoting lines based on Dunedin on the east coast of South Island, starting with a short route up to Port Chalmers. If New Zealand's first mineral railway had echoes of the Festiniog in North Wales, then the new line also had its similarities with that innovative route. Long before Garratt had found his solution to providing enough power to haul heavy loads on narrow-gauge tracks, Robert Fairlie had come up with his solution among the mountains of Wales. It is as well to remember that the decision to adopt the narrow gauge at all was a bold one, for these little railways had all been horsedrawn right up to the 1860s. Fairlie's engines are extraordinary creations, looking like the result of a nasty accident when one conventional engine has reversed into another at speed. Starting at the front is a conventional boiler and engine unit, followed by the cab, after which comes a second boiler and power unit. There is plenty of power, and the two halves are each mounted on bogies to help with tight curves. In 1873, a double-Fairlie worked a train out of Dunedin, just four years after the prototype had run on the Festiniog.

As in Australia, not everyone was happy with this reliance on British expertise, manpower and hardware. There were even more complaints when the next 159-mile route was let to John Brogden & Sons of London for a contract which was to include the provision of rolling stock. What rankled with the New Zealanders was the fact that locals were not given the chance to bid. There were reasons, and sound reasons at that. Although the government was guaranteeing the costs, money still had to be raised on the London markets – New Zealand was too young a country in terms of finance to provide that much cash on its own. It was also still generally believed by many that British expertise was unmatched. And finally, the contractor was expected to bring over a contingent of big, brawny navvies who would stay on as settlers, just as Brassey's men had in Australia. The line was built. However it marked a shift away from British dominance.

Work in the North Island was much slower to develop. The Maoris had no wish to sell, still less to give, their land to the settlers. They went to war and, apart from an uneasy truce in the early 1860s, the wars rumbled on in intermittent campaigns and skirmishes throughout the decade. The result was that some land was captured from the Maoris, and when the wars were over the law took most of the rest. Few Maoris could produce the paperwork to satisfy a European-style court. The way was open to settlement and railways. There was even a workforce available, the Engineer Volunteer Militia, looking for a peace-time role. Brogden again got the pick of the lines. By 1872 negotiation, a somewhat one-sided discussion with the Maoris, was over and land was acquired for expansion. Lines were built in a seemingly haphazard manner, but all pushing outward from centres of population. It began with a 44-mile route into the interior from Auckland, then one linking New Plymouth to the port of Waitara, only 11 miles long this time, but involving 1 in 40 gradients. After that the work shifted to Napier on the east coast and a major through-route to Wellington. At first work went well, but as the builders neared Wellington, they met 'the seventy-mile bush', an area of dense scrub and woodland, scoured by deep valleys. The difficulties met there, however, were as nothing compared with those encountered on the route from Wellington to Masterton.

The need for a railway was obvious, to provide a link between the fertile plain and the coast, but unfortunately the Rimutaka Mountains stood in the way. Experiments in the 1860s with a tramway system quite failed to meet the need, so in 1871 John

Rochfort was authorized to survey this empty country to find a suitable line for a railway. He found a gorge that offered a steep climb for many miles at a more or less steady gradient of 1 in 35, but from the top of the hills there seemed no option but a zigzag, a frightening affair in terms of engineering with severe gradients, tight corners and no fewer than nineteen tunnels. The chief engineer, John Blackett, was not at all keen on the zigzag. He proposed a more direct route down the hill on a 1 in 15 grade using what he called 'special contrivances'. Stationary engines did not seem very practical in remote areas, so he turned instead to the system pioneered in Europe, the Fell Engine (see p. 74).

The Fell system worked, but at a price: a train climbing the 2½-mile incline used as much fuel as it did on the whole of the rest of the 63-mile journey. Because the line was so steep, the engines had to be kept light, weighing in at less than 40 tons, and that had to include the extra weight for the two cylinders and associated gear that drove the 'gripping wheels' which held on to the central rail to give the added traction. There was also extra braking power provided by cast-iron shoes that could be used on the central rail. Even that was not enough braking power, so special Fell brake vans were imported which could also apply brakes to the central rail through a hand-wheel. The strain on couplings during the ascent was quite severe, so that a locomotive was not expected to haul more than 60 tons of passenger stock or 65 tons of freight. By the early twentieth century, trains of 260 tons were the norm, so that when they reached Cross Creek at the foot of the incline, a good deal of remarshalling had to go on. First came a locomotive, followed by a couple of coaches, then another locomotive and two or three more coaches, so that the final train would have perhaps four locomotives spread down its length and a whole string of brake vans bringing up the rear. It would then set off at a stately 6 m.p.h. up the hill. Coming down, the train could be managed by just two locomotives, but required a minimum of five brake vans. It was allowed to gallop along at a giddy 10 m.p.h. The line, opened in 1878, still stands as a striking testimonial to the efficacy of a railway in opening up

247

the country. In an age of motor cars and jet aircraft, the tiny Fell engines hurling tall plumes of smoke into the New Zealand air as they toil up the slope, might seem comical anachronisms. But a century ago, they were the lifelines of a developing, self-confident society.

CHAPTER EIGHT

Conclusion

Within less than half a century of the opening of the world's first public steam railway, all five continents had joined the railway age, and, without exception, Britain had been involved in launching the process. This was not due to either an innate British love of progress or pure altruism: the country prospered greatly from the endeavour. It was not simply a matter of giving employment to the engineers, contractors and navvies who travelled overseas to build the railways. Even more important economically were the orders that flooded in for equipment. Rails, signalling equipment, iron for bridges, material of all sorts was sent wherever construction was in progress – and, of course, rolling stock and locomotives. This book has been primarily about civil engineering, but it would be wrong to end without at least a glance at the steam locomotives that were shipped out from Britain to so many distant lands. When I visited the Rail Transport Museum in New Delhi some years ago, I was inevitably struck by the great preponderance of British machines. Out of twenty-two steam locomotives on display, no fewer than sixteen had been made by British manufacturers. And what an array of names was represented: Kitson, Thompson and Hewitson, DUBS of Glasgow, Sharp Stewart, North British, Vulcan, Robert Stephenson, Beyer Peacock, Sentinel, Nasmyth Wilson, Bagnall and Fowler – a dozen different makers. There were just three steam locos built in India itself. Outside the museum walls, the tracks out of Old Delhi Station still throb under the passage of steam giants, virtually all made in

India. This of course was another aspect of Britain's involvement in world railways: more than merely exporting men and hardware, skills, expertise and knowledge were inevitably passed on.

There seem to have been two distinct types of involvement. First there was involvement in old, developed countries with industries which, if not as well developed as those of Britain, were at least firmly set in place. Mostly these were centres with centuries-long and well-established patterns of settlement. In Europe, countries took from Britain just as much as they needed to kick-start their own systems. In young, self-confident America there was no more than a quick look at the British experience before the locals decided they could manage on their own and would make their own way down different paths. It was in the parts of the world which were coloured red, the lands of the Empire, that the British were to stay longest and achieve most, though even here there were subtle divisions. There were the lands such as Canada and Australia where the indigenous population was pushed aside or, if they resisted, annihilated. Here the settlers rapidly took on a fresh identity as citizens of a new country and, as often as not, began to resent the ties that held them to the mother country. In other cases, and India is the prime example, the British came not as settlers but as rulers. They had no doubt as to their identity, nor where their loyalties lay. Yet despite the differences there runs through this early railway building a current of Britishness, sometimes admirable, sometimes objectionable and occasionally mildly absurd.

There was always something suspect in the notion of exporting British solutions as solutions to fundamentally different problems abroad. It was absurd to manufacture thousands of tons of iron-work to send to Canada to build bridges in the middle of enormous forests. It was absurd to construct cast-iron 'Moghul style' temples in Britain and then send these crude pastiches out to the country which had invented the style: yet Moghul decorations cast in British foundries did grace the railway bridges of India. It was absurd to send out navvies to countries in South America where they were ravaged by tropical diseases, when there was a huge local workforce available completely immune to them. The examples are countless. In part this attitude to the outside world reflects a sense of superiority among the British, confident that no foreigner can do anything as well as they can. In part, at least in the early years, it reflected a nervousness among the overseas backers faced by a, for them, new and untried technology. The British were, of course, usually convinced, and often with justification, that they were the best. Their attitude to foreigners, even when those foreigners were their employers, was not necessarily designed to win friends. An Italian committee who got together to consider Brunel's proposals for the Piedmont Railway received the full Brunelian broadside. He wrote to Babbage, his man on the spot, in 1844:

> It is all so contemptibly childish that it requires some patience to ansr it . . . They go to work as if I had been an operative employed by them to furnish sections & plans of the various lines of Country for them to select and direct – instead of the case being that I was called as a person assumed to be *more experienced & more competent* than they are, and their business only to see on the part of the Govt. that the proposed line is acceptable . . .

Not an attitude likely to endear him to the Italians.

Not every British engineer had the arrogance of Brunel, nor did every British engineer show the supercilious low regard for the 'native' that was all too evident among some of the pith-helmeted pioneers. It is all too easy to denounce the easy sense of superiority, but these were men of their age. They often took with them their wives, who were also of their age, ignorant, very often, of the world into which they were moving, but stalwart and ready to put up with almost any privations to keep their family together. Many suffered badly, bringing up children in a distant land only to see them succumb to one of the many diseases that attacked the British pioneers. Mary Angus, wife of the Scots engineer David Angus, was destined to spend many years in South America, but she set out for Argentina in clothes made of camel hair! Over the years she was to endure a great deal. *En route* to Paraguay with

251

husband and children, the journey began with a 600-mile passage up the River Parana to Asuncion, then continued by rail with the family packed into a goods wagon. This was followed by a night in a filthy hotel with a madman rushing about outside, threatening to kill them all. The next stage was by slow bullock-cart which involved sleeping rough and passing through swamps where the drivers regaled them with cheerful stories of the boa-constrictors which were over 20 feet long and capable of swallowing a bullock. Eventually after days of arduous travel they arrived and were all able to sit down to 'a nice rice pudding'. The women, such as Mrs Angus, were often true heroines, even if their husbands may have been flawed heroes. Few questioned the rights of Europeans to rule over other races, but in this the railway builders were neither more nor less liberal than the majority of their fellow citizens. We should not judge the attitudes of a century ago from the moral standpoint of today. If we do, this whole story becomes one of unbridled commercial imperialism and we lose sight of what were without doubt outstanding achievements.

Britain brought railways to the world. Whatever the motives might have been, the systems they built are a reality that have long outlasted them. The faults of the British were no doubt great, their attitudes sometimes deplorable, but nothing can take away from two irrefutable facts: the labour was enormous; the achievement was immense.

Appendix

It would not be possible, in one book, to list every railway in the world to which the British contributed. But to give at least an inkling of just how wide this network spread, the following list, abstracted from Helps' biography, lists the overseas projects for which William Brassey was the contractor. It includes the names of his partners and of the engineers with whom he worked. Brassey was not necessarily personally involved in each of these contracts. Sometimes, as in Australia, the work was entrusted to one of his agents. It is, nevertheless, a remarkable record and eloquent testimony to the worldwide influence of just one great contractor.

Year	Contract	Partner	Engineer	Mileage
1841	Paris & Rouen	Mackenzie	Locke & Neuman	82
1842	Orleans & Bordeaux	W. & E. Mackenzie	Pepin Lehalleur	294
1843	Rouen & Havre	Mackenzie	Locke & Neuman	58
1844	Amiens & Boulogne	W. & E. Mackenzie	Bazaine & Sir W. Cubitt	53
1847	Rouen & Dieppe	Mackenzie	Neuman & Murton	31
1848	Barcelona & Mataro	Mackenzie	Locke & W. Locke	18
1850	Prato & Pistoja		Italian Government	10

Year	Contract	Partner	Engineer	Mileage
1851	Norwegian	Peto & Betts	Bidder	56
1852	Mantes & Caen		Locke, Neuman, W. Locke	113
1852	Le Mans & Mezidon		Locke, Bergeron	84
1852	Lyons & Avignon	Peto & Betts,	Talabot, Thirion, Molard	67
1852	Dutch Rhenish		Locke	43
1852	Grand Trunk	Peto, Betts, W. Jackson	Ross	539
1853	Sambre & Meuse		Declerq	28
1853	Turin & Novara		Italian Government	60
1853	Hauenstein Tunnel		Etzel	1½
1853	Royal Danish	M. Peto Betts	Etzel, Bidder, G.R. Stephenson	75
1854	Central Italian	W. Jackson, Fell & Jopling	Italian Government	52
1854	Turin & Susa	C. Henfrey	Italian Government	34
1854	Bellegarde Tunnel	Parent & Buddicom	Talabot	2½
1855	Caen & Cherbourg		Locke, W. Locke	94
1855	Coghines Bridge		Italian Government	–
1856	Elizabeth-Linz	M. Peto & Betts	M.C. Keissler	49
1858	Bilbao & Miranda	Wythes, Paxton & Bartlett	Vignoles	66
1858	Eastern Bengal	Wythes, Paxton & Henfrey	Hawkshaw	112
1859	Victor Emmanuel	W. Jackson, Henfrey	Neuman, Ranco	73
1859	Ivrea	C. Henfrey	Italian Government	19
1859	Great Northern, Great Eastern, Great Southern (New South Wales)	Peto & Betts	Whitton	54
1860	Dieppe (laying second road)	Buddicom	Julien	–
1860	The Maremma, Leghorn, &c.,		Pini	138
1860	Jutland	Peto & Betts	Danish Government	270

Year	Contract	Partner	Engineer	Mileage
1862	Mauritius	Wythes & others	Hawkshaw	64
1863	Meridionale	Parent, Buddicomb	Grattoni & others	160
1863	Queensland	Peto & Betts	Fitzgibbon	78½
1863	North Schleswig	Peto & Betts	Rowan	70
1864	Central Argentine	Wythes, Wheelwright, Ogilvie	Woods	247
1864	Lemberg Czernowitz		McClean, Stileman, Ziffer de Herz	165
1864	Viersen-Venlo	Murton	Lange, Bidder	11
1864	Delhi	Wythes, Henfrey	Harrison, Bidder	304
1865	Boca & Barracas	Wythes, Wheelwright	Coghlan	3
1865	Warsaw & Terespol	Vignoles, Ogilvie	Russian Government	128
1865	Chord Line (India)	Wythes & Perry	Rendel	147
1867	Czernowitz Suczawa		Ziffer de Herz	60
1867	Kronprinz Rudolfsbahn	Klein, Schwarz	F. Kagda	272
1870	Vorarlbergbahn	Klein, Schwarz	W. Paravicini	55
1870	Suczawa & Jassy		Ziffer	135

Bibliography

Documentary sources

The Ainsworth Diaries, Rhodes House, Oxford; Brunel Papers, University of Bristol; Mackenzie Papers, Institution of Civil Engineers; Notes and Proceedings, Institution of Civil Engineers; *Railway Gazette*

Books

Acworth, W.M., *Historical Sketch of State Railway Ownership*, 1920
Bayley, Victor, *Permanent Way through the Khyber*, 1939
Berridge, P.S.A., *Couplings to the Khyber*, 1969
Berton, Pierre, *The Impossible Railway*, 1972
Blainey, Geoffrey, *The Tyranny of Distance*, 1968
Brant, E.D., *Railways of North Africa*, 1971
Brereton, Robert Maitland, *Reminiscences of an Old English Civil Engineer*, 1908
Brooke, David, *The Railway Navvy*, 1983
Brunton, *John Brunton's Book*, 1939
Burge, C.O., *The Adventures of a Civil Engineer*, 1909
Burton, Anthony, *The Railway Builders*, 1992
Carroll, B., *The Engineers*, 1988
Castro, Juan José, *Treatise on the South American Railways*, 1893
Chrimes, Mike, *Civil Engineering 1839–1889*, 1991
C.M.H. Clark, *A History of Australia*, Vol. 4, 1980
Clifford, Sir Henry, *Letters from the Crimea*, 1956
Coleman, Terry, *The Railway Navvies*, 1965
Conder, F.R., *The Men Who Built Railways*, 1883
Cumming, D.A., and Moxhan, G., *They Built South Australia*, 1986
Currie, A.M., *The Grand Trunk Railway of Canada*, 1957
Da Silva Telles, P.C., *A History of Brazilian Railways*, 1879
Davidson, G., *The Railways of India*, 1868
Day, J.R., *Railways of Northern Africa*, 1964
— *Railways of Southern Africa*, 1963
E-tu Zen Sun, *Chinese Railways and British Interests*, 1954
Fawcett, Brian, *Railways of the Andes*, 1963
Ferns, H.S., *Britain and Argentina in the 19th Century*, 1966
Fox, Francis, *River, Road and Rail*, 1904
Glazebrook, G.P. de T., *A History of Transportation in Canada*, 1938

Gregory, Robert G., *India and East Africa*, 1971
Hardy, Ronald, *The Iron Snake*, 1965
Hawkshaw, J., *Reminiscences of South America*, 1838
Haywood, Richard Mowbray, *The Beginnings of Railway Development in Russia*, 1969
Helps, Arthur, *Life and Labours of Mr. Brassey*, 1872
Hill, Mervyn F., *The Permanent Way*, 1961
Hodges, J., *Construction of the Great Victoria Bridge in Canada*, 1860
Horrigan, L.J., *Victorian Railways*, 1962
Huddleston, H., *History of the East Indian Railways*, 1926
Joby, R.S., *The Railway Builders*, 1983
Kent, P.H., *Railway Enterprise in China*, 1907
Leggett, R.F., *The First 150 Years of Civil Engineering in Canada*, 1977
— *Railways of Canada*, 1973
Leitch, David B., *Railways of New Zealand*, 1972
Lewis, Colin M., *British Railways in Argentina*, 1983
Lin, Cheng, *The Chinese Railways Past and Present*, 1937
Lloyd, W., *A Railway Pioneer*, 1900
Mackay, Thomas, *The Life of Sir John Fowler*, 1900
Macdonald, Major J.R.L., *Soldiering and Surveying in British East Africa*, 1897
MacGeorge, G.W., *Ways and Works in India*, 1894
Mair, Craig, *David Angus*, 1989
Middlemass, R.K., *The Master Builders*, 1963
Miller, Charles, *The Lunatic Express*, 1971
Morrison, Gabriel James, *A History of the Shanghai and Woosung Railway*, 1879
Nock, O.S., *Railways of Australia*, 1971
— *Railways of Southern Africa*, 1971
Patterson, J.H., *Man Eaters of Tsavo*, 1907
Pauling, G., *The Chronicles of a Contractor*, 1969
Pedlar, Neil, *The Imported Pioneers*, 1990
Peto, Henry, *Sir Morton Peto*, 1893
Pratt, E.H., *State Railway Muddle in Australia*, 1912
Richards, Jeffrey, and MacKenzie, John N., *The Railway Station*, 1986
Richards, Tom, and Rudd, Charles, *Japanese Railways in the Meiji Period*, 1991
Rolt, L.T.C., *Isambard Kingdom Brunel*, 1957
— *George and Robert Stephenson*, 1966
Sanders, E.W.S., *The Military Engineer in India*, 1935
Sanyal, N., *Development of Indian Railways*, 1936
Satow, Michael, and Desmond, Ray, *Railways of the Raj*, 1980
Shelford, Anne E., *The Life of Sir William Shelford*, 1909
Singleton, C.C. and Burke, D., *Railways of Australia*, 1963
Skeat, W.O., *George Stephenson and His Letters*, 1973
Smith, J.B., *Railways for Bombay*, 1848
Stevens, G.R., *Canadian National Railways*, 1960
Stone, E.H., *The Nizem's State Railway*, 1876

BIBLIOGRAPHY

Thompson, George, Norman, V., and Edgar, J.H. *Canadian Railway Development*, 1933

Thorner, Daniel, *Investment in Empire*, 1950

Trevithick, Francis H., *The History and Development of the Railway System in Japan*, 1894

Vignoles, Olinthus, J., *Life of Charles Blacker Vignoles*, 1885

Walker, Charles, *Thomas Brassey*, 1969

Webster, N.W. *Joseph Locke*, 1978

Weithal, L.C., *The Story of the Cape to Cairo*, 1923

Westwood, J.N., *Railways of India*, 1974

— *A History of Russian Railways*, 1964

Wilson, Roger Burdett (ed.), *Sir Daniel Gooch Memoirs and Diary*, 1972

Woodcock, George, *A Social History of Canada*, 1988

Wright, Winthrop R., *British-Owned Railways in Argentina*, 1974

Young, Robert, *Timothy Hackworth*, 1923

258

Index